DR. THOMAS SYDENHAM (1624–1689)

Other studies in medical history by the same author

The Quicksilver Doctor: The Life and Times of Thomas Dover, Physician and Adventurer, John Wright and Sons, Ltd., Bristol, 1957.

John Locke (1632–1704), Physician and Philosopher: A Medical Biography with an Edition of the Medical Notes in his Journals, Wellcome Historical Medical Library, London, 1963.

An engraving of Mary Beale's portrait of Thomas Sydenham, reproduced from the first edition of his *Observationes Medicae*, etc. (1676).

KENNETH DEWHURST

Dr. Thomas Sydenham (1624-1689)

His Life and Original Writings

UNIVERSITY OF CALIFORNIA PRESS
BERKELEY AND LOS ANGELES
1966

PUBLISHED IN THE UNITED STATES OF AMERICA
BY THE UNIVERSITY OF CALIFORNIA PRESS
BERKELEY AND LOS ANGELES, CALIFORNIA

LIBRARY OF CONGRESS CATALOG CARD NUMBER: 66–19348

THIS WORK IS ALSO PUBLISHED IN THE UNITED KINGDOM
BY THE WELLCOME HISTORICAL MEDICAL LIBRARY, LONDON

Printed in Great Britain

Contents

List of Illustrations

Preface

IT is high time that Dr. Thomas Sydenham's extant writings were presented in their original English as nearly three centuries have passed since they were published. Sydenham's English was translated into Latin by various friends, and hence, all previous editions of his works are, in fact, retranslations. Therein the simple, robust vigour of his seventeenth-century prose is masked beneath the rhetorical sophistications of his translators' Latin, and the stylistic niceties of Latham's best-known Victorian edition (1848–50). Other English editions by Pechey (1696) and Swan (1742) are now difficult to obtain, as also is J. D. Comrie's *Selected Works of Thomas Sydenham* (1922). Based as they are on unoriginal texts these retranslations fail to do full justice to the greatest physician this country has ever produced. The sound judgement and acute observations of Thomas Sydenham, the English Hippocrates, freed clinical medicine from the last vestiges of medievalism, and set the pattern for further progress. There is, therefore, ample justification for presenting these fragments of Sydenham's original writings together with his correspondence. And although the occasional letter and essay have been published previously, their inclusion here is, I think, warranted as earlier sources are not readily available. Most of his manuscript writings are presented here for the first time.

The only English biography[1] of Thomas Sydenham, by Dr. J. F. Payne, was published in 1900 and is now out of print. Since then, some new biographical material has come to light, particularly in the Lovelace Collection of John Locke's papers, and this has now been incorporated into the life of Sydenham which precedes this edition of his writings.

Thomas Sydenham came to medicine more by accident than design: he fully shared in the military and political vagaries of his family's fortune. His eldest brother, Colonel William Sydenham, was a founder of the Protectorate and one of the handful of men holding supreme power during Cromwell's military dictatorship. Having signed Richard Cromwell's proclamation, he soon changed sides, and, as one of the leaders of the Wallingford House Party, engineered a *coup d'état* which ended Richard's brief rule. Thomas Sydenham loyally supported his brother throughout the vicissitudes of civil war and the bewildering

[1] A French biography of Sydenham by L. M. F. Picard was published at Dijon in 1889.

flux of its political aftermath. And his loyalty to the "Good Old Cause" eventually brought him government patronage. Revolution and its convulsive political aftermath were irresistible distractions to the peaceful pursuit of medicine during these unquiet times. It was not until the Restoration that he began his important study of the London epidemics. These early aspects of his career have, hitherto, been only scantily presented. Yet only when his whole life is surveyed within its historical setting can an explanation be found for the constant criticism of which he so bitterly complains throughout his medical writings.

In the preparation of this book I am particularly indebted to Mr. Alastair McCann for checking and transcribing several original manuscripts. I would also like to thank Lieutenant-Colonel the Lord Wynford, M.B.E., for showing me round Wynford Eagle Manor; the Wellcome Trustees for their financial support; Mrs. D. E. M. Birtles for typing the manuscript, and Mr. L. M. Payne, Librarian of the Royal College of Physicians of London, for kindly showing me several college manuscripts. Dr. Donald G. Bates has also kindly checked some of the manuscripts. I am also most grateful to Mr. W. W. Robson, Fellow of Lincoln College, Oxford, who has eliminated several errors from the typescript and made some useful suggestions for improving it; and to Dr. F. N. L. Poynter, the series editor, for making a number of corrections while seeing the work through the press.

Oxford
December 1964

PART I

1. Wynford Eagle Manor House, Dorset, where Thomas Sydenham was born in 1624. (*By kind permission of* Country Life, *London.*)

The Fighting Sydenhams

INCREASING specialization and the perfection of scientific techniques cognate to medicine have overshadowed the art of clinical practice. Yet, in its ultimate resort, physic must always be more of an art than a science: the aetiology and treatment of nervous illnesses, individual variations in pain threshold, and unpredictable responses to treatment, do not readily lend themselves to the scientific tape-measure. Although scientific techniques have greatly accelerated the general progress of medicine, particularly in the diagnostic sphere, technical gadgets can never completely replace those qualities of acute observation, clinical experience, and balanced judgement which make up the mature physician. Nor can the clinical art be acquired in libraries or laboratories. And the quality of medical practice is well-nigh impossible to assess by formal examinations which preclude the candidate from ignoring whatever is useless. This gulf between the art of practice and the infant medical sciences existed even in the seventeenth century when Thomas Sydenham practised. The discoveries of Galileo, Sanctorius, Borelli and the stimulus of Descartes caused the iatrophysical "school" of physicians to liken the body to a machine, whereas their colleagues of the iatrochemical school under the leadership of Paracelsus, van Helmont, Glauber, and Sylvius interpreted bodily processes as a series of chemical reactions. Both these schools of experimentalists greatly contributed to medical progress, although they tended to push reasonable hypotheses to unreasonable limits. Thomas Sydenham's great merit lay in avoiding these new highways of speculation as well as the well-beaten track of Galenic orthodoxy: instead, he concentrated on perfecting the art of practice by a plain, historical approach to clinical problems, thereby placing the art of medicine upon a sound basis of probability. He had many advantages. As a young soldier during the Civil War Sydenham gained a deep insight into the vagaries of human nature. Later, he was spared the dull necessity of having to make a diligent study of erroneous textbooks in order to pass formal examinations. Puritanism caused him to take sides against the King of England, and when practising as a physician he rebelled against all that was useless in orthodox medicine: the idea that only the *useful* was *good* was characteristic of seventeenth-century Puritanism.

Thomas Sydenham was born in 1624 and baptized on 10 September at Wynford Eagle, a hamlet of Toller Fratrum, eight miles west of Dorchester. The Sydenhams, descended from an old Somersetshire family, had been settled in Dorset since the reign of Henry VIII, and their manor house, restored in 1630 by Thomas's father, William Sydenham, is still standing.[1] In 1611 William Sydenham had married Mary, the orphan daughter of Sir John Jeffrey of Catherston, by whom he had three daughters, Mary, Elizabeth, and Martha, and seven sons. Two sons died in infancy, and most of the others had brief and stormy lives. Thomas, the fifth son, lived the longest. But such are the vagaries of time that the military and political exploits of William, the eldest son, which brought him both fame and notoriety in his lifetime, are now completely forgotten, whereas Thomas Sydenham's reputation only reached its zenith after his death. After a brilliant career in the Parliamentary army, William Sydenham became Governor of Weymouth and the Isle of Wight, a Member of Parliament, and one of the founders of Cromwell's Protectorate. Two other brothers, Francis and John, were killed while serving as majors in the Parliamentary army, and Richard, who had been an army captain, died soon after hostilities ended.

Although details are lacking, it is not difficult to imagine Thomas Sydenham's boyhood as the younger son of a country gentleman. His life would doubtless follow a regular pattern of field sports, schooling, and religious devotions. And early in life he would be taught to ride; to breed and train hounds; to handle a sword, and to shoot with musket and pistol. The Sydenham children probably first benefited from the services of a private tutor, and later the brothers may have attended Dorchester Grammar School in order to acquire sufficient Greek, Latin, and Mathematics to take them to Oxford. But his sisters' educational pattern would have been quite different. The seventeenth-century squirearchy did not encourage the scholastic aspirations of their daughters whom they regarded as little more than auxiliary housekeepers. They stitched, spun, cooked, brewed wine, and fed the ducks: in due season they married and went their way.[2] On 1 July, 1643, when he was seventeen[3] years old Thomas Sydenham entered Magdalen Hall, Oxford, whose Principal, John Wilkinson, was one of the leading Puritans in the University. William Sydenham had already left Trinity College without taking a degree, and Thomas did not long pursue his studies in tranquillity, as within two months of his university

[1] A. T. Cameron (ed.), *The History of the Sydenham Family* (1928), p. 225.

[2] Martha Sydenham married Mr. Lawrence of Wraxhall, a prominent Parliamentary lawyer; her sister Mary married a Mr. Lee (John Hutchins, *The History and Antiquities of the County of Dorset* (1863), vol. II, p. 202).

[3] Joseph Foster (ed.), *Alumni Oxonienses* (1892), vol. IV, p. 1449.

admission, the conflict between King and Parliament reached its final catastrophe. Dorset was strongly on the side of Parliament. Before the King raised his standard at Nottingham on 22 August, 1642, Poole and Dorchester (the latter described by Clarendon as "the great seat of disaffection") were being hastily fortified by volunteers to the Parliamentary cause. William and Francis Sydenham were amongst them, and they were later joined by their father.

Why did the Sydenhams, as landed gentry, so zealously rally to the side of Parliament? Professional historians are still hotly disputing the causes of the Civil War, and their differences have been summarized by Christopher Hill.[1] Gardiner interpreted the war as a struggle for religious and constitutional liberty. Contemporary historians have more respect for Clarendon's account. He believed that the war was simply a struggle for power in which religious differences were relatively unimportant. And recently economic issues have also come to the fore. Professor Tawney[2] suggests that the Revolution was caused by the rise of the gentry before 1640, whereas Professor Trevor-Roper[3] cogently argues that the gentry were then passing through an economic crisis. Hence their revolt against the administrative and economic centralization of the capital: the Civil War was a protest by the declining gentry against a privileged bureaucracy and a capitalist city. Recently, in his Ford Lectures, Mr. Hill[4] has traced the great ferment of ideas, stemming from Puritanism in its widest sense, which helped to prepare men's minds for revolution. He has shown how Bacon, Raleigh, and Coke brought a refreshing spirit of free inquiry, based on reason and experience rather than authority, into science, history, and the law.

A study of local history reveals several causes of discontent in Dorset. The county had suffered heavily from the King's arbitrary taxation: its long seaboard led to a high levy of Ship Money, and in 1632 the local Justices of the Peace complained that "this little county" was taxed equally with Hampshire and Wiltshire.[5] Puritanism flourished in the county. The fervent preaching of the Reverend John White, Rector of Holy Trinity, Dorchester, caused one hundred and forty local Puritans to seek religious freedom in America where they founded Dorchester, Massachusetts. Finally, when the Irish rebels seemed likely to prevail, the gentry petitioned the King in February 1642, as they feared a foreign Papist invasion, to which the county was highly vulnerable.

[1] Christopher Hill, *Puritanism and Revolution* (1958), pp. 3–31.
[2] "The Rise of the Gentry", *Economic History Review* (1941), XI, no. 1.
[3] H. R. Trevor-Roper, "The Social Causes of the Great Rebellion", *Historical Essays* (1958), pp. 195–205.
[4] Christopher Hill, *Intellectual Origins of the English Revolution* (1965).
[5] A. R. Bayley, *The Great Civil War in Dorset* (1910), p. 3.

How many of these, often contradictory, explanations caused the Sydenhams to be drawn into the vortex of civil war? Probably several provocations combined to spark off their revolt. As devout Puritans the Sydenhams felt bound to follow the teachings of the King of Kings rather than the "divinely" inspired notions of the King of England. And they were sorely vexed by the many Royal unconstitutional acts. They may well have been labouring under several other unascertainable provocations. At least we *know* that they opposed their King with more courage and tenacity than any other family in the county of Dorset.

Thus, after barely two months at Oxford, the war caused Thomas Sydenham to join his family in the Parliamentary army. It was here, in the bitter clash of opinion and conscience which divided his fellow-countrymen on the battlefields of Dorset, that he came to manhood. And these years of soldiering were to prove more important in his development than any academic knowledge gained in the placid arena of the University: the bitter experiences of irregular warfare inculcated a sturdy independence, a self-reliance, and a strong practical bias which set the pattern of his later life, as well as imposing certain limitations upon it.

The Civil War in Dorset was a series of localized skirmishes having only a secondary connexion with the pitched battles which finally decided the conflict. Nevertheless, both sides waged war with the utmost ferocity. Situated between the Royalist strongholds of the south-west and their headquarters at Oxford, the county was of considerable geographical importance. The coastal towns with their useful harbours and proximity to France were a vital link in the Royalist communications with their continental allies. The battle for Dorset was virtually a series of skirmishes, cavalry raids, and sieges in which the two armies were so evenly matched that whenever one side was able to spare troops from elsewhere, they rapidly made large territorial gains. Apart from the superiority of numbers, success greatly depended upon efficient and reliable intelligence whereby cavalry commanders were able to strike with the all-important element of surprise. During most of the campaign the Parliamentary cavalry was led with great daring by Francis Sydenham, under whom Thomas served as a Cornet.[1] As the most junior officer in the regiment he carried the colour like an Ensign of Foot.

At first all went well for the Parliamentarians. With Poole and Dorchester heavily fortified, they captured the Royalist stronghold of Sherborne and, by May 1643, only Corfe Castle remained in Royalist

[1] Proof of Thomas Sydenham's commission is to be found in C. H. Mayo (ed.), *The Minute Books of the Dorset Standing Committee* (1902), p. xxxii.

2. Speed's map of Dorsetshyre, 1610.

3. Corfe Castle, Dorsetshire.

hands. On a misty morning a party led by Sir Walter Earle with Captain William Sydenham as second-in-command surprised and captured the town of Corfe. Establishing their headquarters in the church, the Parliamentarians bombarded the castle, but failing to reduce the defences, they resorted to "stratagems and engines". A rudimentary tank was constructed consisting of a "sow" and a "boar": the latter being a boarded contraption lined with wool to deaden the shot, while the "sow" (designed to protect the invaders) was made of timber bound together with hoop-iron and roofed with hides.[1] The doors and windows at the front of the machine were kept firmly shut until the walls of the fortress were reached, whereupon the attackers hoped to leave by the rear of the vehicle. But this primitive tank, mounted on wheels and propelled by a series of levers, failed to breach the defences. Scaling-ladders were brought, and volunteers for an assault party were called for. Prizes were offered for the first man to reach the walls, but when monetary inducements failed to gain a response, the soldiers were liberally plied with drink in the hope that drunkenness would make "men fight like lions, that being sober would run away like hares".[2] Eventually, a frontal attack was mounted and immediately repulsed by Lady Bankes and her few defenders, who showered them with hot embers and large stones. Hearing that Bristol had fallen to Prince Rupert, and disheartened by the prolonged siege, Sir Walter Earle withdrew from the scene leaving Sydenham in command. As a strong Royalist force under Prince Maurice rapidly advanced into Dorset, Sydenham was forced to raise the six weeks' siege of Corfe and withdraw to Poole. On 2 August, 1643, Dorchester meekly surrendered to Lord Carnarvon. But the victorious troops, completely disregarding the terms of surrender, treated the disaffected residents with such licence that Carnarvon resigned his command in protest, and returned to support the King at the siege of Gloucester. Lord Goring then took over, and even Clarendon records that his ruthlessness brought greater discredit on his cause. In the autumn the whole of Dorset, with the exception of Poole and Lyme, "two little fisher towns", was in Royalist hands. And Prince Maurice, having failed to take them, withdrew, leaving Lord Crawford to reduce these recalcitrant ports.

During this rapid Royalist advance William Sydenham senior was captured, and held prisoner in Exeter. Fortunately, he had provided for his eldest son to wage war as is shown by the terms of a covenant between them drawn up on 5 July, 1643. He was bound to his father

[1] Thomas Perkins and Herbert Pentin (eds.), *Memorials of Old Dorset* (1907), p. 210.
[2] George Bankes, *The Story of Corfe Castle* (1853), pp. 187–8.

for the payment of £559, of which £90 had already been repaid. The son agreed to provide the balance by supplying one hundred and thirty sheep, one hundred and sixteen lambs, five rothers, eight steers and heifers in lieu of £100; the sale of sixty acres of oats for a further £100. He also agreed to pay another £100 and one year's rent for land at Wynford Eagle. This debt was finally settled on 10 August, 1644.[1] William Sydenham had to wait two years longer for the £150 which he subscribed to Parliamentary funds. On 28 September, 1646 the Dorset Committee[2] ordered a partial refund from "Lady Strangway's rent" which was sequestered Royalist property captured by his sons.

The Sydenham brothers, defending Poole against superior Royalist forces, were then sorely in need of financial and military assistance. Indeed, Francis, quartered in the house of a Royalist sympathizer, was constantly complaining about the losses he had incurred in the service of Parliament whose fortunes were then at their lowest ebb. His landlady judged that he might be induced to change sides. A secret meeting was arranged, and Sydenham was promised a free pardon, the reimbursement of his losses, and promotion to the rank of major if he agreed to assist Lord Crawford in capturing Poole. Having partially agreed to these Royalist overtures, Sydenham received his pardon and £40 on account. It was decided that he would leave the town gates unlocked. At the appointed time Lord Crawford arrived at the head of eight troops of Horse and two Foot regiments. "All is our own, on, on!" exclaimed Sydenham, and the Royalists rushed into the town. The gates suddenly closed, exposing the invaders to a withering broadside of musketry and artillery: they were only saved from annihilation by the fact that the gates had been closed too soon, and the Parliamentary cannon were too highly sighted. In this attack the Royalists lost twenty men, fifty horses, and three hundred arms.[3]

After this defeat the Royalists withdrew from the neighbourhood of Poole, as Parliamentary cavalry began to take up the initiative. Francis Sydenham raided Purbeck Island, returning with three hundred and twenty-three cattle to feed the garrison. While one Parliamentary force was threatening Wareham, another led by Francis Sydenham made a diversionary attack on Wimborne to prevent the Royalist garrison there from coming to their assistance. Wareham was thus regained for Parliament on 23 November, 1643; and a month later, Sydenham led a more daring raid on Dorchester. He apprehended the Deputy Governor, freed all political prisoners, raided an ammunition depot, and "confiscated" gold plate from the local goldsmith. Sydenham

[1] A. R. Bayley, *op. cit.*, Introduction, p. 37.
[2] C. H. Mayo, *op. cit.*, pp. 2–3.
[3] A. R. Bayley, *op. cit.*, p. 117.

returned to Wareham with his entire force of one hundred men within an hour and a half. But he was not so fortunate when he led a raid on Holmebridge and engaged a strong detachment of Lord Inchquin's regiment in an indecisive battle lasting nearly five hours in which both sides suffered heavy casualties.[1]

In the spring of 1644 the contest still favoured the Royalists. They regained Wareham, and Prince Maurice began the long and unsuccessful siege of Lyme Regis. Francis Sydenham contacted Sir William Waller who sent reinforcements so that the siege was raised in June 1644. Shortly afterwards Weymouth and Melcombe fell to Lord Essex, who appointed William Sydenham, now a colonel, as Governor.[2] Essex asked Sydenham to prevent the Royalists from using Wareham as a base for raiding parties; and in the same letter mentioned the good news of his father's release.[3] The old man was soon in action. In July Colonel O'Brien led a raiding party of two hundred and fifty Royalist Horse and Foot from Wareham to Dorchester in the hope of ransoming the town for £1,000. Having reached the outskirts of Dorchester, the Royalists delayed their attack, which gave the inhabitants time to summon help from Weymouth. A strong party led by the Sydenham brothers (including their father serving as a captain under his eldest son) set out to their relief. Taken by surprise the Royalists were heavily defeated, losing twelve killed and one hundred wounded or captured, amongst whom were eight Irishmen. In this engagement "old Captain Sydenham who had been a long time the enemy's prisoner in Exeter behaved himself very bravely".[4] His eldest son then ordered the Irishmen to be given such quarter "as they gave the Protestants in Ireland". They were duly hanged, "one of them being spared for doing execution on his fellows". Sydenham's ruthlessness was sanctioned by Essex who agreed to the execution provided they be "absolute Irish", as "he would not have quarter allowed to those".

About this time (July 1644) a tragic event embittered the Sydenham family. Mrs. Sydenham was killed by a party of Royalist Dragoons commanded by Major Williams. The circumstances are unknown, but she was probably killed in a reprisal raid on her home. Major Francis Sydenham, her second son, avenged her death a few months later when a Royalist party attacked Poole and then "vanished like a vaporous cloud". With a force of fifty to sixty horsemen "double pistolled", he pursued them to Dorchester, and then charged the whole regiment

[1] *Ibid.*, p. 123.
[2] John Rushworth, *Historical Collections* (1691), pt. iii, vol. II, p. 683.
[3] Essex's correspondence with Colonel Sydenham during 1644 is to be found in B.M., Add. MS. 29319, ff. 4–8, 11 and B.M., MS. Eg. 2126, ff. 11–14.
[4] John Hutchins, *op. cit.*, vol. II, pp. 343–4.

through the town. He beat them back a second time "most stoutly charging upon the Dragoons and crying out to his soldiers: 'Give the Dragoons no quarter!'". After a third charge Sydenham found himself facing Major Williams who advanced towards him at the head of a troop of Horse. Recognizing him as the officer who had "basely and cruelly" killed his mother, Sydenham "spoke to his men that were next to him, to stick close to him, for said he, 'I will now avenge my Mother's innocent blood, or die in this place'; and so he most valiantly made his way to Major Williams, and slew him in the place, who fell down dead under his horse's feet".[1]

Elsewhere, the differences between the two sides were expressed in less savage incidents. Dr. Bowles, a Royalist physician of Oundle, was called to treat a Parliamentary captain suffering from dysentery. The latter had just torn up some Common Prayer books—whether as a protest against orthodoxy, or on account of the limitations imposed by illness on a man of action, is not related. But the doctor caused the leaves of the prayer book to be boiled up in milk and administered to his patient. When this preparation wrought a rapid cure, the doctor proceeded to discourse on the misfortunes of tearing up a book with such striking medicinal properties. To a sceptic who inquired whether any other sort of printed paper would not have done just as well, the doctor replied: "No, I put in the prayer for the visitation of the sick."[2]

In the summer of 1644 the tide of Royalist successes, which had flowed so steadily throughout the county in the preceding year, now began ebbing fast. Towards autumn the Parliamentary forces led by the Sydenhams intensified their raids. In August Francis successfully defended Dorchester, while William and Sir Anthony Ashley Cooper captured Wareham. Francis attacked Bridport, but his cavalry was beaten off with some losses; a month later he stormed Axminster. Meanwhile on 30 October, Colonel Sydenham "had a brave bickering with the Royalist at Crew taking 100 Horse and 40 prisoners".[3]

Sir Anthony Ashley Cooper (later the first Earl of Shaftesbury), who had left the Royalist cause and was then commanding a Parliamentary brigade, joined forces with the Sydenham brothers in an attack on Abbotsbury House, the residence of Sir John Strangways. The contest raged with great fury for over six hours as the defenders refused to surrender. Ashley Cooper ordered the house to be set on fire, and directed his soldiers to aim at the windows to prevent anyone from escaping. As the house began to blaze, the besieged Royalists called out for quarter. Ashley Cooper refused to take them prisoner, but the

[1] John Vicars, *The Burning Bush not Consumed* (1646), pp. 72–3.
[2] R. T. Gunther, *Early Science in Cambridge* (1937), p. 267.
[3] John Vicars, *God's Arke* (1646), p. 62.

The fortifications of Weymouth and Melcombe when the Royalists attacked on 7 February, 1645

4. The fortifications of Weymouth and Melcombe when the Royalists attacked on 7 February, 1645.

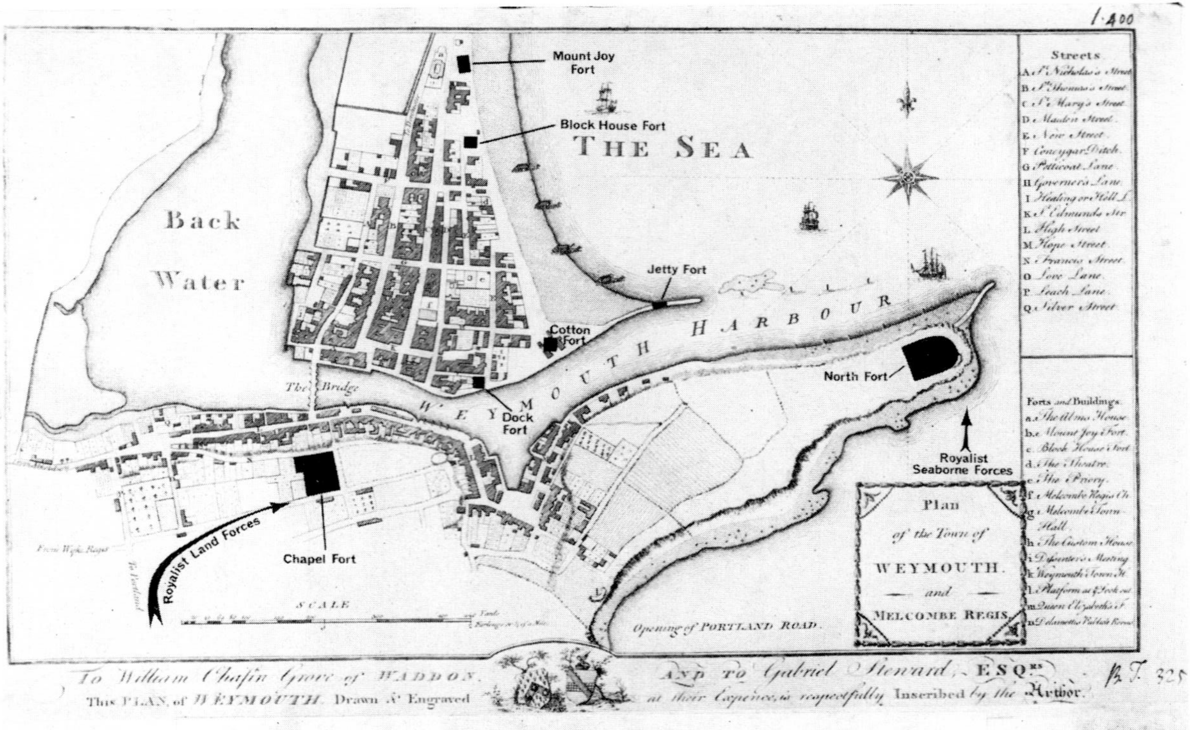

Sydenham brothers, who had been attacking from the other side, allowed them to surrender. This incident led to a dispute between Colonel Sydenham and Ashley Cooper, causing the latter to make a formal complaint. But the County Committee reaffirmed their confidence in Sydenham by appointing him Commander-in-Chief in Dorset, and his brother Francis was given command of the county cavalry.

So far Thomas Sydenham has not been mentioned in contemporary chronicles. He was not a commander and did not write the dispatches. Hence he failed to get into the history books. But he undoubtedly took part in most of his brother's raids, and early in 1645 was stationed in Weymouth.

The coastal towns were now under Parliamentary control, and the castles of Portland, Corfe, and Sherborne were held by strong Royalist forces. Colonel Sydenham had strengthened his headquarters of Weymouth by ringing the port with a series of forts, the strongest being the Chapel Fort situated on a hill dominating the town, and overlooking an arm of the sea.[1] Melcombe was relatively unguarded, as Weymouth was considered to afford sufficient protection for both towns, which were connected by a drawbridge. At midnight on 7 February, 1645, while the Parliamentary garrison of Weymouth was reposing under a false sense of security, the Royalists attacked. One party, travelling by land, gained the Chapel Fort, and a seaborne force simultaneously attacked the key fort facing Portland. Major Francis Sydenham rallied his men and led a counter-attack on the Chapel Fort. In this futile action he was severely wounded, and most of his men were captured. Francis Sydenham died the next morning and was buried by Peter Ince,[2] Minister to the garrison, who wrote: "His death was no small joy to our enemies to whom he was a perpetual vexation and terror, and no small grief to us who had our eyes too much upon him."

Meanwhile, Colonel Sydenham had succeeded in evacuating most of his men into Melcombe. He raised the drawbridge between the two ports and then set about strengthening the meagre defences of Melcombe. While awaiting an attack he sent off urgent messages for reinforcements. But the Royalists made the mistake of regarding Melcombe as indefensible, and Clarendon described Sydenham's troops as no better than "prisoners at mercy". They first tried to reduce Melcombe by cannon-fire, but a week's fruitless bombardment accomplished little more than intensifying their enemies' fire. Then they tried to burn down the town by firing red-hot slags across. Several houses were set ablaze, but Sydenham countered these tactics by

[1] C. H. Mayo, *op. cit.*, p. 504, states that William Sydenham senior provided £40 towards the defence of Weymouth which was repaid on 9 February, 1649.

[2] Peter Ince, *A Brief Relation of the Surprise of the Forts of Weymouth* (1644/5), pp. 3–4.

sending a raiding party into Weymouth where they burned down several houses. Both sides then tried to build up overwhelming forces. From Poole Sydenham got two hundred and eighty men by sea, and a hundred cavalry by land. Strengthened by troops from Lord Goring's Dorchester garrison, the Royalists decided to take Melcombe by storm but, as Goring drew up his troops for the attack, Sydenham fired enemy shipping in the port and burned down several houses. These diversions, accompanied by an intense Parliamentary bombardment, caused the attack to be postponed. The contest again lapsed into a stalemate.

The Battle of Weymouth saw two of the foremost medical men of the seventeenth century unwittingly opposing each other across the narrow strip of water which separates the twin towns. Thomas Sydenham, then a cavalry officer, but destined to become the leading British physician, was in Melcombe, while Richard Wiseman, Surgeon to a Royalist Foot regiment in Weymouth, later became the foremost practical surgeon in England. They were both kept busy: Sydenham leading cavalry raids and Wiseman treating casualties. The latter mentioned attending a soldier who "by the grazing of a canon shot, had the fore-part of his head carried off", yet he survived for seventeen days until he "fell into a Spasmus and dyed, houling like a dog, as most of those do who have been so wounded".[1] Wiseman also treated a maid with a head wound who lived until the brain "was wrought out or corrupted";[2] and a soldier shot through the heel whose severe haemorrhage he successfully controlled with cautery after other methods had failed. But the surgeon's most detailed description concerned the amputation of a soldier's hand.

I was called at break of day to an Irish-man [he wrote], of Lieutenant Coll. Ballard's Regment, who in shooting off his musquet, brake and tore his hand to pieces after a strange manner: I purposed to cut off his hand; I sent presently to my quarters to one of my Servants to bring a saw, and knife, and dressing, of which at these times we had always stores, which being brought, I took a red ribbon from my case of Lancets, and bound upon his Arm some four fingers above the Carpus, and cutting the flesh, bared the bones of their membrane; I divided the flesh between the bones, and setting the saw close to the flesh above, I sawed it off, and untied my Ligature above, and bringing down the musculous flesh and skin over the end of the bone, not making any cross-stitch, have drest up that stump with my Restrictives, and rouled him up, and returned again to my quarters. I had not been an hower gone, but I was sent for again to this Irish-soldier, he being as the messenger said grievously full of pain; I wondered at it, and hastened away, before I came to his hut, I heard him crying, I asked him what he ailed to roar so, it was a while before he would answer me,

[1] Richard Wiseman, *A Treatise of Wounds* (1672), p. 134. [2] *Ibid.*

at last he told me he was not able to indure that red Ribbon that I tied his Arm with; I was at first herein surprized, to think I should leave the Ligature upon his Arm, that being a sure way to bring a Mortification upon the part: I put my hand in my pocket, and shewed him the red Ribbon on the Case of Lancets, he seemed at first to doubt it, but after he see it was so, he laught; and was from that time in ease. . . .[1]

Colonel Sydenham was the first to take the initiative. While a small party of cavalry were escorting a Royalist convoy of provisions into Weymouth, he sent out a cavalry detachment, including his brother Thomas, to harass them. The Royalists were routed. They lost sixty prisoners and, in the disorderly retreat, abandoned their supplies. In this engagement Thomas Sydenham was the only Parliamentary casualty.[2] While he was having his wounds dressed in Melcombe, the Royalists moved a large force of infantry out of Weymouth in order to retrieve their stores. But once the Royalist infantry were clear of the town, Colonel Sydenham attacked the Chapel Fort with a strong force. This unexpected assault on a weakened post caused the Royalists to retreat in disorderly confusion as is apparent from Wiseman's account:

Our men were surprized [he wrote],[3] and chased out of the Town and Chappel Fort; I was at the same time, it being about twelve a clock, dressing the wounded in a house for that purpose in the Town, almost under the Chappel and Fort, I heard a woman cry, fly, fly, the Fort is taken: I turned aside a little amazed, towards the Line, not knowing what had been done; when I got upon the Line, I see our people running away and those of the Fort shooting at them, I slipt down this work into the ditch, and got out of the Trench; and as I began to run, I heard one call Chirurgeon, I turned back, and seeing a man hold up his stump and his hand I thought it was the Irish-man, whom I had so lately dismembered; I returned and helpt him up and we ran together, it was within half musquet-shot of the enemies Fort, he out ran me quite. . . .

Colonel Sydenham then set about consolidating his position, and by evening both towns were again under his command. Undismayed, Lord Goring decided to counter-attack Melcombe at several points simultaneously. But details of the Royalist plans reached Sydenham the day before by an escaped prisoner. The weather also favoured the defenders, as it was a clear night on 28 February, 1645, when Goring's troops were seen approaching. Their main assault was directed against the west of the town, and in accordance with a prearranged feint,

[1] Richard Wiseman, *op. cit.*, pt. II, pp. 101–2.

[2] Contemporary accounts mention the wounding of Colonel Sydenham's brother in a cavalry skirmish. As Major Francis Sydenham had been killed this must have referred to Thomas Sydenham as the other brother served in the infantry.

[3] Richard Wiseman, *op. cit.*, pt. II, pp. 101–2.

Colonel Sydenham ordered his men to withdraw after offering only slight resistance, while the townsmen gave the invaders entry through their back doors. Under the impression that they had gained an easy victory the Royalists poured into Melcombe, whereupon Sydenham counter-attacked with all his force, driving them across into Weymouth. After two hours of bitter hand-to-hand fighting the Royalists retreated to Wyke Regis having lost two hundred and fifty men and a large quantity of stores and ammunition. This action ended the Battle of Weymouth after eighteen days' fierce fighting, during which the Parliamentary forces had "neither put off their arms nor their clothes". And Sydenham's nine hundred men, who had repulsed an onslaught of four thousand Royalists, were voted £2,000 by a grateful Parliament. A service of thanksgiving was preached before both Houses of Parliament by the Reverend John Arrowsmith.

It would be most strange and ominous [he declared],[1] if the Church should not be found upon her knees, now when Rome and hell are conspiring against her: if when three Kingdoms are beleagur'd by Popish confederates, they should not be garrison'd with praying Saints.

And the congregation were reassured that God was on their side. "Let him therefore be styled, at least for this day, the God of our Parliament and of their forces at *Scarborough*, at *Shrewsbury*, and at *Weymouth*."

As soon as he had secured Weymouth, Colonel Sydenham ordered Captain John Cade and John Mills to be court martialled for treachery in allowing the Royalists to gain entry during their initial attack. They were found guilty and sentenced to death. Their conviction caused Sir Lewis Dives, the Royalist commander, to warn "Master Sydenham" that reprisals would be taken against his family should the men be executed.

Be best assured that, if you put to death these innocent persons [concluded Dives], I will vindicate this blood to the utmost of that power wherewith God shall enable me, upon you and yours, without ever giving quarter to any one who hath relation to you, which shall faith fully be performed by him that professeth himself your enemie. . . .

In his reply Sydenham outlined the principles for which he and his family were fighting.

You desire me to look upon my own heart [he replied], which I have done, and find written there, in the fairest characters, a true desire of advancing God's honour, maintaining the King's just power, and contending for the

[1] John Arrowsmith, *England's Eben-Ezer* (1645), pp. 15, 21.

privileges of the Parliament at Westminster, and the liberty of the subject. . . . May it please your Worship to be merciful too, if not to him, yet to me and mine (when we fall into your hands); till when your last experience might remember you that I am as far from fearing as my present condition is far from needing your quarter, which I hope I shall have an opportunitie to dispute further of with you; whom to any man in England I shall answer to this quarrell.[1]

The appeal for clemency was ignored and the two prisoners were hanged. Sydenham was just as ruthless with his own men: he ordered a trooper to be burned through the tongue for swearing,[2] and encouraged the detection of other offenders by getting his soldiers to report one another.

The recapture of Weymouth virtually ended Royalist resistance in Dorset, and Thomas Sydenham was now free to resume his interrupted studies. Although he decided to return to Oxford, he had not formed any plans as to his future career. On his way there he visited his sick brother, then under the care of Dr. Thomas Coxe.[3]

With his well-known kindness and condescension, Dr. Coxe asked me what pursuit I was prepared to make my profession [wrote Sydenham[4] many years later], since I was now returning to my studies, which had been interrupted, and was also arrived at years of discretion. Upon this point my mind was unfixed, whilst I had not so much as dreamed of medicine. Stimulated, however, by the recommendation and encouragement of so high an authority, I prepared myself seriously for that pursuit.

Sydenham returned to his old college, Magdalen Hall, but after a few months, transferred to Wadham.[5] The University was completely disorganized. In the spring of 1647 Parliament appointed Visitors (all fervent Puritans) to purge the Fellows who refused to take the Covenant, or in any way opposed the ruling powers. There was, of course, much opposition amongst Royalist supporters, and a year of conflicts, disputes, and dismissals passed before Oxford again became the centre of learning, more or less subservient to the will of Parliament. Sydenham's name occasionally appears in the Registers as a supporter

[1] A. R. Bayley, *op. cit.*, p. 245.

[2] *Ibid.*, pp. 317–18.

[3] Dr. Thomas Coxe, M.A. (Cantab., 1638), M.D. (Padua, 1641), F.R.C.P. (1649). He had been a physician in the Parliamentary army, and became President of the College of Physicians in 1682. One of the original Fellows of the Royal Society, Coxe was removed from the presidency of the College of Physicians on account of his Whiggish tendencies. Anthony Wood, *Fasti Oxonienses* (1815), vol. II, col. 93, and William Munk (ed.), *The Roll of the Royal College of Physicians of London* (2nd. ed., 1878), vol. I, p. 247.

[4] Thomas Sydenham, *The Works* (1848), ed. R. G. Latham, vol. I, p. 3.

[5] Montagu Burrows, *Register of the Visitors of the University of Oxford, 1647–1658* (1881), p. 561, and confirmed by Sydenham in a letter to Dr. Gould dated 10 December, 1687 (B.M., Add. MS. 4376, f. 75).

of the Visitors, and on 30 September, 1647 he was appointed one of their delegates for Wadham College. Vacant Fellowships passed to firm Parliamentarians. But many potential candidates for offices had been unable to qualify themselves for the necessary degrees by the ordinary course of residence and exercises in the Schools, so to satisfy their aspirations, as well as to provide sufficient candidates, a large number of degrees were conferred by "creation". This usually meant that the candidate was voted a degree by Convocation, occasionally subject to the satisfactory performance of certain exercises, but frequently without any conditions. Anthony Wood referred to this method of receiving a degree as "the Pembrokian Creation" after the Earl of Pembroke, the University Chancellor. Thomas Sydenham was one of the fortunate recipients, being created Bachelor of Medicine on 14 April, 1648, barely a year after his return.[1] He was then elected to a Fellowship at All Souls in place of an ejected Royalist, and a few months later was appointed Senior Bursar of his college.[2] He also received arrears of army pay when the Dorchester Parliamentary Committee, of which his brother William was a member, passed this resolution on 20 April, 1648:[3]

Commission Officers reduced.

It is ordered that the Treasurer of the county shall pay unto these officers, here under named, after the same proportion that the other reduced officers of this county are appointed to bee payd by a late order of this Committee betwixt this and Mycmas, viz. . . .

Cornett Tho. Sydenham	06.13. 4
Lieut. John Sydenham	10. 0. 0.

As Sydenham had completed little more than eighteen months in a confused and unsettled University, his appointments are best regarded as belated military honours rather than academic distinctions: he was officially a medical don, though in fact still a medical student.

The stern realities of the Civil War, the military occupation of the city, and the dispossession of Parliamentary, and later Royalist Fellows, had unsettled the tranquillity of the University. Many of the new undergraduates were more interested in facts gained from observation and experiment than in the disputations and rhetorical displays which had pleased their fathers. And within the next decade some of these talented interlopers caused Oxford to sparkle anew with their experimental ingenuity. The mathematicians Wallis and Ward came from Cambridge in place of unyielding Royalists; Dr. Jonathan Goddard,

[1] Anthony Wood, *Athenae Oxonienses* (1820), ed. Philip Bliss, vol. IV, col. 270.
[2] C. Grant Robertson, *All Souls College* (1899), p. 124.
[3] C. H. Mayo, *op. cit.*, p. 386.

Cromwell's Physician, was appointed Warden of Merton; Dr. William Petty was then Tomlins Reader in Anatomy,[1] and Dr. Wilkins of Wadham (married to Cromwell's sister) became the leader of a group of experimental philosophers forming the nucleus of the Royal Society. Amongst Sydenham's contemporaries at All Souls were Christopher Wren and Dr. Thomas Millington, later President of the College of Physicians: it was Millington who stated that Sydenham's absence from the University had caused him to forget his Latin, so he set about revising it by constantly reading Cicero.[2]

Although there were many individual experimentalists in Oxford, the official University teachers remained as undistinguished as the medical curriculum was antiquated. Sir Thomas Clayton, the Professor of Medicine, was "possest of a timorous and effeminate humour, and could never endure the sight of a mangled or bloody body":[3] he was supposed to lecture twice weekly from the texts of Hippocrates and Galen, but these slender duties were often carried out by proxy. Botany could be studied under Jacob Bobart in the Physic Garden; and Dr. William Petty demonstrated anatomy on the bodies of newly executed criminals during the Lent term. Sydenham soon realized that the medical curriculum, over-burdened with theory, was only vaguely related to the physician's primary task of treating the sick: there was no training in clinical medicine. So he read the works of Hippocrates with profit and interest, but on the whole he was bored with the mixture of classical learning, anatomical dissections, and formal disputations which made up the medical course. Apparently he voiced his opinions on medical education to a contemporary student, John Ward,[4] who later became Vicar of Stratford-on-Avon. "Physick says Sydenham, is not to bee learned by going to Universities, but hee is for taking apprentices; and says one had as good send a man to Oxford to learn shoemaking as practising physick." Sydenham's utilitarianism, stemming partly from Puritanism, and stimulated by Bacon's writings, was shared by some of his contemporaries who were then busily investigating the infant sciences. Although Sydenham had many friends amongst these early scientists he never joined them in busy experiment: he failed to realize that their work was destined, many years later, to accelerate the progress of clinical medicine.

[1] The Tomlins Readership in Anatomy was held by the Regius Professor of Medicine, Sir Thomas Clayton, who in 1650 resigned in favour of his deputy, Dr. William Petty (H. M. Sinclair and A. H. T. Robb-Smith, *A Short History of Anatomical Teaching at Oxford* (1950), p. 12).

[2] *The Family Memoirs of the Rev. William Stukely, M.D.* (1882), Surtees Society, 73, vol. I, p. 70.

[3] Anthony Wood, *op. cit.*, vol. IV, col. 215.

[4] *Diary of the Rev. John Ward, M.A. (1648–1679)* (1839), ed. Charles Severn, p. 242.

One sensational incident concerning the revival of a woman hanged for murdering her child could hardly have failed to escape his notice. After being duly declared dead by the Sheriff, she was "stretched out in a coffin in a cold roome and Season of the year", when a lusty fellow detecting her breathing, "stamped on her breast and stomach severall times with all the force he could".[1] Aubrey[2] gives this account of her resuscitation: "Anno Domini (1650) happened that memorable accident and experiment of the reviving of Nan Greene a servant maid who was hang'd in the Castle of Oxon for murdering her bastard-child. After she had suffer'd the Law, she was cut downe and carried away in order to be anatomiz'd by some young physitians." The two doctors, William Petty and Thomas Willis, gave her "hot and cordiall spirits", took off five ounces of blood, tickled her throat with a feather, and "put her to bed to a warm woman". The undergraduates collected for Anne Greene (who married and had several children) and celebrated her macabre deliverance in doggerel verses, one of which ends with this couplet:

Thus 'tis more easy to recall the Dead
Than to restore a once-lost Maidenhead.

Oxford did not long enjoy the services of one of the revivalists as Petty joined Cromwell's Irish army as Physician-General. But anatomy's loss was more than compensated by his immense contributions to political economy, or "political arithmetick" as he called it. Also on his way to Ireland was Captain John Sydenham, a younger brother, then serving in Colonel Stubbe's regiment which had been ordered on 21 May, 1650 to march from Kent to Chester. It is not known whether the prospects of the long march undermined Sydenham's troops, or the attractions of easy loot proved irresistible, but they were an undisciplined rabble. They plundered Sir James Harrington's property at Uxbridge, which caused the Council of State to reprimand their commander. At Oxford, John Sydenham called on his brother, from whom he borrowed money to buy six horses and generally equip himself. When he eventually led his men into action in Ireland, their earlier misdemeanours were forgotten, and Sydenham was promoted major at the beginning of 1651 when only twenty-five years old.

The cause for which the Sydenhams had fought so hard was not

[1] R. Watkins, *Newes from the Dead or a True and Exact Narration of the Miraculous Deliverance of Anne Greene*, etc. (1651).

[2] *Brief Lives and Other Selected Writings* (1949), ed. A. Powell, p. 269. Anne Greene's escape from death is also reported in: *The Diary of John Evelyn* (1955), ed. E. S. de Beer, vol. IV, p. 57; *The Petty Papers* (1927), ed. Lord Lansdowne, vol. I, pp. 157–67; F. Madan, *Oxford Books* (1931), vol. III, nos. 2151, 2153, 2158–62 and Plot, *Oxford-shire* (1677), pp. 197–9.

flourishing as well as they had hoped. In 1648 there had been Royalist risings in South Wales, Essex, and Kent; and in August of that year Cromwell defeated Hamilton's Scottish army at Preston. War in Ireland dragged on until 1649 when Cromwell's whirlwind campaign brought red victory, although a large army remained in that unhappy country. Likewise the political front seethed with unrest. Victory found the Sydenhams in a political minority. They were Independents, or more specifically Army Independents, an influential group of gentry which included most of the high-ranking officers.[1] Both Colonel Sydenham and his father sat in the Long Parliament and, with other Independents, they constantly opposed Presbyterian demands for a reduction in the armed forces. They also favoured an extension of religious toleration, another major issue which brought them into conflict with the Presbyterians: it was on this subject that Colonel Sydenham made the most important Parliamentary speech of his career. But as country gentlemen the Sydenhams were much more conservative than the majority of their fellow Independents. Colonel Sydenham had been one of the tellers in the minority of the Long Parliament who favoured retaining the House of Lords: he also upheld the retention of the Established Church and the Universities. As men of property the Sydenhams had not opposed the King in order to bring about upheavals in the social hierarchy, and they must have been particularly alarmed at Army attempts at democracy by the Levellers and the more radical Diggers. Having led a successful revolution the Army Independents found themselves opposing a Presbyterian Parliamentary majority and trying, at the same time, to dam back the great flood of revolutionary ideas amongst their own radical soldiery which they had so lately helped to unleash. Through their hold over the army the Independents triumphed over both their adversaries. Colonel Pride brought them to power when he forcibly excluded one hundred and forty undesirable Members of Parliament, leaving only a remnant of fifty to sixty including Colonel Sydenham. Shortly after this *coup d'état* the execution of the leading Levellers put an end to Army democracy, and when the Rump Parliament was threatened by Charles Stuart's Scottish army the Sydenhams rallied to its support. While Colonel Sydenham played a prominent part in the Parliamentary arena, Richard, as "Commissioner for the Fee Farm Rents", was one of the civil servants responsible for raising the funds to keep the army in the field; John, who was already serving in Ireland, was transferred to

[1] Details of Colonel Sydenham's religious and political associations are to be found in George Yule's *The Independents in the English Civil War* (1958), p. 119. As Colonel Sydenham achieved political advancement he rewarded his brother Thomas, who presumably held similar political opinions.

Cromwell's army in Scotland, and on 21 April, 1651 Thomas rejoined as a Captain of Horse in the 1st Militia regiment commanded by Colonel Rich.

Soon after joining his regiment in Essex, Sydenham had a remarkable escape from death. One night a drunken trooper burst into his room, grasped Sydenham with one hand, and fired a pistol at his chest from close range. Fortunately for the future of British medicine, the bullet shattered the assailant's left hand, and Sydenham escaped unscathed.[1] The soldier may well have been disgruntled through lack of pay, as about this time the Council of State urgently ordered the Army Committee for Essex to pay Captain Sydenham's company, which was now ready to march on active service.[2] There was a further delay as his company was not up to full strength, and the Essex Militia Commissioners were ordered to complete the establishment so "that he being complete may attend the service of the Commonwealth to which he is commanded, and which cannot bear delay".[3]

The campaign on which Thomas Sydenham now embarked was totally different from the territorial skirmishes of Dorset. His unit was one of many regiments under Cromwell's grand strategic plan. First it was held as a mobile strategic reserve, while Cromwell vainly tried to engage the Scottish army in a decisive battle in the Highlands. In May 1651, when Sydenham's regiment was ordered to lie in the neighbourhood of Leicester and Nottingham in order to secure the Midland counties, Cromwell brought the Scots to battle at Stirling where Major John Sydenham was mortally wounded. But the main Scottish army slipped past Cromwell's forces and headed for the Border. Anxious to prevent a winter war "to the ruin of our Soldiery, for whom the Scots are too hard, in respect of enduring the Winter's difficulty of that Country",[4] Cromwell ordered Sydenham's commander to join forces with Major-General Harrison's regiment and "embody upon the borders", ready to serve in either country. Sydenham's regiment did, in fact, cross the Border as many years later he mentioned making up a gallon of medicine for treating colic in Scotland,[5] which suggests that he physicked his men as well as leading them into action. As the southward march of the Scottish army continued, Colonel Rich's force endeavoured to shadow them and impede their progress, without committing themselves to a total engagement against overwhelming forces. Leaving General Monk in

[1] Andrew Broun, *A Vindication of Dr. Sydenham's New Method of Curing Continual Fevers* (1700), pp. 81–2.

[2] C.S.P. (Dom.), 1651, p. 195.

[3] *Ibid.*, p. 191.

[4] B. Whitelocke, *Memorials of the English Affairs* (1672), p. 501.

[5] *Anecdota Sydenhamiana* (1845), ed. W. A. Greenhill, p. 73.

command in Scotland, Cromwell ordered Lambert's cavalry to harass the rear of the Scottish army so that his main body of infantry could catch up.

Apart from minor skirmishing, the Scots met with only slight resistance until they reached Lancashire. It was then decided to prevent them from crossing the Ribble at Warrington Bridge. The only forces available to resist the Scots were Harrison and Rich's four thousand Horse, and three thousand local Militia which were ordered to defend the bridge. But the Scots brushed aside the Militia, and crossed with the King at their head. Just south of Warrington, Colonel Rich's cavalry were ordered to attack the King's Life Guards. The Parliamentarians "wheeled off Parties and charged them thrice as they came on, and the Lord caused the Enemy every time to fly before us. The Scots counter-attacked shouting: 'Oh you Rogues, we will be with you before your Cromwell comes,' which made us think they would press to engage us with all speed."[1] But the Parliamentary cavalry, mustering six thousand now that Lambert's regiment had joined them, were still unwilling to engage, as their "horses could not do us service for the Inclosures". So they withdrew to Knockforth Moor, near Lancaster, where the open heathland was ideally suited for manœuvring cavalry. Again Colonel Rich's regiment endeavoured "to amuse the Enemy and to flank and front them",[2] but the Scots, ignoring the challenge, marched on southwards during the night. Realizing that Prince Charles was making for Worcester, a detachment of cavalry were sent on ahead to prevent him from garrisoning the town. As Sydenham's troop had constantly been in the vanguard of the earlier engagements, he may well have been included in this party which was soon overwhelmed by the invaders. As the Scots began fortifying Worcester, Parliamentary cavalry were deployed round the town in order to await the arrival of Cromwell's main force. At Evesham the latter was joined by Fleetwood's troops, and after a few days skirmishing the Battle of Worcester began, on 3 September, 1651. After fierce infantry hand-to-hand fighting, Cromwell broke the Scottish army by nightfall, though he described the fight as "a stiff business". Royalist prisoners were herded into the Cathedral, and the gory scene seems to have affected Harrison, as "the dead Bodies of Men and the dead Horses of the Enemy filling the Streets, there was such a nastiness that a Man could hardly abide the Town".[3] Colonel Rich's regiment was ordered to pursue the retreating remnants, and amongst their two thousand prisoners was Richard Wiseman, who was not as fleet of foot

[1] B. Whitelocke, *op. cit.*, p. 502.
[2] *Ibid.*, p. 505.
[3] *Ibid.*, p. 508.

as he had been at Weymouth. He was taken to Chester where his surgical dexterity was soon called upon. "Whilst I was a prisoner at Chester, after the Battel of Worcester," he wrote,[1] "I was carried by Coll. Duckenfield's order to a substantial man, that out of too much zeal to the cause pursuing our scattered forces, was shot through the joynt of the Elbow, from the lower and outerpart of the os Humeri, out below, between the Ulna and Radius, he had laboured six weeks under great pain" . . . before Wiseman successfully amputated the limb.

Only a thousand[2] Scots returned home after the battle, and if Whitelocke's too partial account can be trusted, the Parliamentary army lost only one hundred soldiers killed, three hundred wounded, and two officers killed, with "Captain Howard and another Captain wounded". Could this unnamed officer have been Thomas Sydenham? He was again wounded during this campaign, but details are lacking. Many years later, when telling Dr. Andrew Broun of how on several occasions he narrowly escaped death, Sydenham mentioned that he had been "left on the field among the dead".[3] And elsewhere he wrote that his army service had resulted in "the loss of much bloud", and he was thereby "much disabled".[4] There were three possible occasions when Sydenham may have been wounded: the skirmish at Warrington Bridge, the attempt to prevent the occupation of Worcester, or during the Battle of Worcester; and the phrase "left on the field" suggests a pitched battle rather than a cavalry skirmish.

When he recovered, Thomas Sydenham returned to Oxford where he soon became friendly with the Honourable Robert Boyle. Their friendship was the most important feature of Sydenham's Oxford career: it was Boyle who first kindled his interest in the study of epidemic diseases, and several years later, when Sydenham was investigating the London epidemics, he interpreted their nature partly in terms of Boyle's favourite corpuscular theory. But at this stage in his career his brother's increasing political importance prevented Thomas Sydenham from devoting all his energy and interest to medicine.

In the spring of 1653 Cromwell cast aside the thin veil of constitutionalism and ordered the army to turn out the Rump Parliament. Colonel Sydenham favoured this "interruption", which irrevocably divided civilian and military supporters of the Republic. He was duly elected to the succeeding Nominated or Barebones Parliament, made up of members nominated by Church congregations and approved by

[1] Richard Wiseman, *op. cit.*, pt. II, p. 97.
[2] B. Whitelocke, *op. cit.*, p. 507.
[3] Andrew Broun, *op. cit.*, p. 81.
[4] C.S.P. (Dom.), 1654, p. 14.

the Army Council. This assembly legislated through a number of standing committees, and Colonel Sydenham served on those concerned with the "Propriety of Incumbents in Tithes", "the Advancement of Learning", and the Committee for the Army and Navy.[1] It was probably through his influence that Richard Sydenham was appointed a commissioner for collecting and disbursing revenues to clergy.[2] But the constant bickering between the radical impractical idealists and the conservative army officers which made up Barebones Parliament soon led to its dissolution. As Colonel Sydenham played a leading part in the intrigues which brought down Parliament he can be regarded as one of the founders of Cromwell's Protectorate which succeeded it. General Lambert, Sydenham, and other officers made their plans in secret: subterfuge was essential as they were a minority. Assembling at the House of Commons before their opponents arrived, Sir Charles Wolseley lost no time in moving: "That the Sitting of the Parliament any longer as now constituted would not be for the good of the Commonwealth, and that, therefore, it is requisite to deliver up unto the Lord General Cromwell the Powers they have received from him."[3] Colonel Sydenham seconded the motion, and a debate began. Fearing the arrival of Opposition Members the Speaker did not wait to put the question, but left the House with those favouring the motion. Soldiers were then sent to put the other Members out. An "Instrument of Government" was drawn up by the army officers vesting Cromwell and his Council of State with executive powers. But when Colonel Sydenham was offered an appointment as a member of Cromwell's Council of State, he came upon an unexpected impediment. All members were asked to swear an oath of fidelity to Cromwell. Sydenham held out for several months until the fruits of office proved more tempting than the perverse luxury of a Puritan conscience. The financial rewards were great.[4] His salary was £2,000 a year, and he had already received £1,000 and sequestered Royalist lands towards arrears of pay.[5] Having arranged his brother Richard's appointment as a "Commissioner of Fee Farm Rents", he now used his influence to help Thomas gain some compensation for the losses incurred during his military service. On his brother's advice, Thomas Sydenham now

[1] H. A. Glass, *The Barebones Parliament* (1899), pp. 91, 92.

[2] *Ibid.*, p. 121.

[3] E. R. Turner, *The Privy Council of England, 1603–1784* (1928), vol. I, p. 303.

[4] Colonel Sydenham served on many committees. At various times he was a member of the committees for foreign affairs, foreign plantations, safety, Scottish affairs, Treasury, and a Commissioner for the Admiralty and Navy (E. R. Turner, *op. cit.*, vol. II, pp. 243–57). That he took these duties seriously is shown by the fact that between 1 November, 1655 and 26 June, 1656 he attended ninety-eight meetings of the Privy Council (*ibid.*, vol. I, p. 320).

[5] Mark Noble, *Memoirs of the Protectorate House of Cromwell* (3rd ed., 1787), vol. I, p. 397.

petitioned Cromwell[1] directly. His appeal was granted on 25 April, 1654, when the Revenue Committee was instructed to pay him £600 out of funds in the keeping of the Commissioners for Coal Duties in the port of Newcastle;[2] they were also requested to "give him such employment as he is most capable of".[3] This reference to the possibility of government employment shows that Thomas Sydenham then had other plans of earning a livelihood than practising medicine.

Apart from his friendship with Boyle, Sydenham gained little academically during the three years of Oxford residence after his return from the Battle of Worcester. But his Fellowship did provide him with free accommodation and a salary without the necessity of teaching, or even residing, in Oxford. He was frequently away visiting his brother in London, or his father at Wynford Eagle. While in Dorset he met Mary Gee, and, with his newly gained financial independence, he resigned his Fellowship and married her at Wynford Eagle in 1655. He was thirty-one years old. Soon afterwards Sydenham bought a house on the site of the Ram's Mews in King Street, Westminster, and began to practise as a physician.[4] It was along this principal thoroughfare of Westminster that Charles I had passed on his way to trial, as did Cromwell also, first to Parliament, and later, to absolute power. Sydenham had chosen a position favourable for obtaining practice, preferment, and patronage. Near the Protector's Court at Whitehall, his house was in the district where his brother and most of the government officials resided, while behind lay the swampy marshes of St. James's Park which periodically provided him with an influx of malarious patients. It was a politicians' residential area rather than one favoured by doctors.

The beginning of Sydenham's medical practice can be verified from his own writings. It was about 1655 or 1656 that he tried his prentice hand in the treatment of a case of dropsy. "I well remember (for it was the first time I was called upon to treat a dropsy)", he wrote[5] in 1683, "having been summoned twenty-seven years ago or thereabouts, to a worthy married woman named Saltmarsh at Westminster." At first his practice was small and uncertain, whereas the excitement of the ever-changing political scene, which he had in some small measure helped to bring about, and wherein his brother was now playing an increasingly important role, was all-absorbing.

The struggle between the central authority (vested in the Protector

[1] P.R.O., S.P. Interregnum, vol. lxvii, f. 37, and C.S.P. (Dom.), 1654, p. 14.
[2] C.S.P. (Dom.), 1654, p. 115.
[3] *Ibid.*, p. 33.
[4] Mackenzie E. C. Walcott, *Westminster: Memorials of the City*, etc. (1849), p. 70.
[5] Thomas Sydenham, *Tractatus de Podagra et Hydrope* (1683), p. 148.

and his Council of State) on the one hand, and the right of Parliament to exercise some control over taxation and the army, on the other, led to military dictatorship. This was inevitable. Retreat by the central authority before Parliament's challenge was quite impossible, as the military executive's authority rested solely on their control of the army. But the leaders of this military cabal having broken irrevocably with the radical left, had also vexed the conservative gentry by centralizing the functions of local government which had always been their traditional role. Ironically the political wheel had now come full circle, and the usurpers of power were abusing their authority as much as Charles I had done in 1642. The issue of religious toleration further aggravated the dissensions between the executive and Parliament. The generals were in favour of a greater degree of religious freedom than were the majority of Members of Parliament, who showed their hostility towards government policy in their savage persecution of the Quaker, James Naylor. The essence of the Naylor debate was whether to sentence him to death by Bill of Attainder, or hand him over to the judicial power. Parliament had no judicial powers under the Constitution. Naylor was duly arraigned before a specially appointed committee in the Painted Chamber of the House of Commons. And amongst the visitors to his trial was a young Oxford undergraduate, John Locke, who informed his father that he had seen Naylor and his women followers with their gloves on, humming and exhorting each other. Locke thought that Naylor was mad, and failed to understand his defence which was delivered in uncouth language. Thomas Sydenham was also there to hear his brother make an eloquent speech in support of the executive's policy. "We live as Parliament men but for a short time," declared Sydenham, "but we live as Englishmen always. I would not have us to be so tender of the privilege of Parliament as to forget the liberties of Englishmen."[1] He then submitted that Naylor was more in need of a physician than a gaoler. But Naylor was flogged, branded, and bored through the tongue before Cromwell intervened and demanded to know under whose authority Parliament had acted. The trial convinced Cromwell of the necessity of having a Second Chamber with powers to judge between the Protector and Parliament when differences arose over the interpretation of the Constitution.[2] Cromwell, of course, favoured an amenable Upper House, and Sydenham's strong support of his policy in the Naylor debate made him an obvious choice. "My Lord Protector is under an oath to maintain the laws," argued Sydenham,[3] "and all the articles of

[1] Thomas Burton, *Diary* (1828), ed. J. T. Rutt, vol. 1, p. 274.
[2] C. H. Firth, *The House of Lords during the Civil War* (1910), p. 246.
[3] Burton, *op. cit.*, vol. 1, p. 246.

the Instrument of Government. Is not he then to look so far to the good and safety of the people as to see that no man be sentenced but by these laws, not without or against them?"

On Sydenham's elevation, a Republican pamphleteer remarked that though "he hath not been thorough-paced for tyranney in time of Parliaments, it was hoped he might yet be so redeemed as never to halt or stand off for the future against the Protector's interest".[1] Colonel Sydenham was now a famous and powerful man, mentioned by Milton, Latin Secretary to the Council of State, in this passage: "And I will add some whom thou hast summoned to be thy councillors, men famous for political wisdom and the arts of peace, and who are known to me by friendship or repute; Whitelocke, Pickering, Strickland, Sydenham and Sidney."[2] Thomas Sydenham closely supported his brother's political career, and in 1658 offered himself as a candidate for Weymouth. But Cromwell died before an election could be held.

At the beginning of Richard Cromwell's reign the struggle for power split the participants into three main groups: the Commonwealth Party supported by most of the inferior army officers; the Protector's entourage backed by officers serving in Scotland and Ireland; and the Wallingford House Party to which Colonel Sydenham and most of the high-ranking officers belonged. With Fleetwood, Desborough, and Berry, Sydenham was one of the ringleaders of this military cabal, named after their meeting-place, the London residence of Charles Fleetwood.[3] When writing to Henry Cromwell within three weeks of his father's death, Falconbridge named Sydenham, Berry, and Huson as "the close contrivers".[4] And Father Thomas Talbot[5] in a letter to Lord Ormonde of 6 May, 1659 aptly described Colonel Sydenham as "a very factious man and one of the Godly party, though not the wisest statesman . . .".

Dr. Thomas Sydenham supported his brother by standing as one of

[1] *The Harleian Miscellany* (1809), ed. T. Park, vol. III, p. 478.

[2] Milton's description of Sydenham as famous in "the arts of peace" might be called poetic licence, as throughout the struggle between Parliament and the Army he constantly favoured military dictatorship. "Col. Sidnam, who had been 6 weeks from us", wrote TB, a newswriter, on 8 April, 1657, "and all the dissatisfyed party, came thronging in with their negatives, and thought to have carryed it cleare. Some talke that they have a further designe to discreditt this modell, by bringing in one of their owne more illustrious, and more answering the ends propounded. It would doe well, if we could come to a settlement at any hand, but its hardly to be hoped for, if this fayle. Sword dominion is too sweet, to be parted with, and the truth is (whatever kind of squeesynes we may pretend to) that the single issue, the maine dread is, that the civill power shall swallow upp the millitary: there's a Demetrius in the case I doubt." (*The Clarke Papers* (1901), ed. C. H. Firth, vol. III, pp. 104–5.)

[3] Godfrey Davies, *The Restoration of Charles II, 1658–1660* (1955), p. 74.

[4] Sir James Berry and Stephen G. Lee, *A Cromwellian Major-General* (1938), p. 209.

[5] *Calendar of Manuscripts of the Marquess of Ormonde, K.P.*, Historical Manuscripts Commission (1902), n.s., vol. I, p. 328.

the seven candidates for four vacancies in the twin towns of Melcombe and Weymouth in the January 1659 elections to Richard Cromwell's Parliament.[1] Military dictatorship had changed public opinion to such an extent that the majority of Members of the new Parliament were men of moderate views, Presbyterians rather than Independents, and absolutely opposed to a continuation of Army rule. Sydenham was probably identified by the electorate with his brother's well-known militarism as he was not elected to what was virtually the family seat. Nevertheless, Colonel Sydenham intensified his intrigues against Richard Cromwell. The Protector refused to accede to the officers' demands for more control over the army. There was plot and counter-plot. Whereas Oliver Cromwell's power depended on army support, his son failed to gain their allegiance, and a crisis came in the spring of 1659. The leaders of the Wallingford House Party presented the Protector with an ultimatum to dissolve Parliament. Their demands were accompanied with a martial flourish, and, as the troops obeyed their commanders, Richard Cromwell was out-manœuvred into political oblivion. Parliament was dissolved, and Members were excluded by soldiers. As a reward for his intrigues in gaining Republican support in this bloodless *coup d'état*, Sydenham was made a member of the Committee of Safety and given command of one of Richard Cromwell's former regiments.[2] He had now reached the zenith of his political importance, and in the summer of 1659 arranged for his brother to share in the spoils of office. Dr. Thomas Sydenham was made Comptroller of the Pipe, which was not a urological appointment, but a department of the Exchequer concerned with the registration of Crown leases.[3] It was a sinecure requiring few, if any, duties to supplement his income from medical practice.

It has been suggested, on slender evidence, that Thomas Sydenham went to Montpellier just before the Restoration to study under the famous Protestant physician, Charles Barbeyrac. This statement rests entirely on the hearsay evidence of M. Desault,[4] an eighteenth-century French surgeon who mentioned that one of his friends had met Sydenham at Montpellier. Once accepted, this story has constantly been recounted without any attempts at verification. But did Sydenham ever visit France? He had just been appointed to a lucrative government post at home, and would be unlikely to leave so soon afterwards. He never named Barbeyrac in any of his writings, nor did he mention

[1] John Hutchins, *op. cit.*, vol. II, p. 433.
[2] Godfrey Davies, *op. cit.*, pp. 75–86. *The Journals of the House of Commons* (1659), vol. VII, pp. 683 and 688.
[3] C.S.P. (Dom.), 1659–60, p. 29.
[4] P. Desault, *Dissertation sur les Maladies Vénériennes*, etc. (1733), p. 359.

setting foot in France. He simply described his movements as follows: "After a few years spent in the arena of the University, I returned to London for the practice of medicine."[1] Fifteen years after the Restoration John Locke, physician and philosopher, spent three and a half years in France, and lived for eighteen months in Montpellier, as a close friend of Dr. Barbeyrac. Locke corresponded every month with Dr. John Mapletoft who sent him news of their common friend, Sydenham. In none of these letters, nor in two other letters actually written by Sydenham to Locke during the latter's residence abroad, does Sydenham send his regards to Barbeyrac, or even mention his name. There is also evidence to show that Sydenham did not understand French. When thanking Locke for sending him a French abridgement of his famous *Essay Concerning Human Understanding*, Dr. David Thomas wrote:[2] "You cannot expect much concerning your booke from Dr. Sidenham or Goodall who neither understand the language it is writt in." Sydenham naturally expected all foreigners to learn English, and he even regarded addressing a letter in French as a great imposition. "I made your Complement to Dr. Sydenham who would return it under his hand," wrote Mapletoft to Locke,[3] "but that he cannot prevayl with himself to write A Monsieur Monsieur which he rayles at as a very impertinent way of adres." Is it really likely that Sydenham, with such a strong streak of chauvinism, and his deeply ingrained Puritanism, would ever leave his family, practice, and government post to visit Catholic despotic France? It is fairly certain that he never left England, and it was Barbeyrac who was influenced by Sydenham's writings: indeed, one of Locke's friends mentioned that Barbeyrac "commends extreamely by Dr. Sydenham's book".[4]

He was probably also concerned about his brother's struggle to retain power as the partnership between the Army leaders and the Rump Parliament progressed uneasily through the summer of 1659. It was ruffled by Sir George Booth's Royalist rising in Cheshire, suppressed by Lambert. Another crisis came in the autumn when Parliament withdrew the commissions of several leading officers, whereupon Lambert's troops secured the Mint and the Treasury; the sword ruled naked, and not entirely unashamed. Meanwhile, Monk had secretly agreed to bring his Scottish army to Parliament's support. Lambert marched north to meet him but his unpaid troops melted away, and the remnants returned to defend Westminster. Colonel Sydenham also rejoined his regiment and marched on the City. When asked to

[1] Thomas Sydenham, *Works*, ed. R. G. Latham, vol. I, p. 3.
[2] B.L., MS. Locke, c. 20, f. 64.
[3] *Ibid.*, c. 15, f. 212.
[4] *Ibid.*, c. 5, ff. 22–3.

explain this display of sabre rattling before the Council of State he tried to justify violence by "undertaking to prove that they were necessitated to make use of this last remedy by a particular call of the divine Providence". Bradshaw, a dying man and impatient of humbug, interrupted the Colonel and expressed "his abhorrence of that detestable action, and telling the council, that being now going to his God, he had not patience to sit there to hear his great name so openly blasphemed".[1] The game was up for Colonel Sydenham and the Army grandees. And when Monk reached the capital he discharged him "as one disagreeable to him". "Colonel Sydenham who had been one of the members of the Committee of Saftey," wrote Rugg,[2] "and very active, was by Parliament desired to returne home, for that they had no service for him to doe, and not to returne in to the Citty except [by] an order by them. So hee went in to Dorsettshire, it being the place of his aboade." At the Restoration Colonel Sydenham was one of twenty (excluding the Regicides) to be excluded from the benefits of the Act of Indemnity, and was declared perpetually incapacitated from holding any office or public employment. For a time he lived at Clapham, where he was denounced for using seditious language likely to disturb the peace of the kingdom and compelled to give a bond of £1,000.[3] An ailing man, crushed by the downfall of his party and the collapse of his cause, he returned to Wynford Eagle in the summer of 1661, attended by his brother Thomas. He died there in July, his widow surviving him by barely a week. When a few months later his father died, Thomas Sydenham returned to London as the sole survivor of a family whose name would now be more of a liability than an asset.

As his brother's political associate, Thomas Sydenham had neither the inclination nor the inducement to devote all his energies to medical practice. Politics came first during these turbulent years before the Restoration swept him from office and sharply reversed his family's fortune: henceforth medicine was to be his sole concern.

[1] Edmund Ludlow, *Memoirs* (1894), vol. II, pp. 140–1.
[2] W. L. Sachse (ed.), *The Diurnal of Thomas Rugg (1659–61)*, (1961), p. 30.
[3] C.S.P. (Dom.), 1660–1, pp. 320, 426.

The Physician

UPON Boyle's "persuasion and recommendation", Sydenham began the clinical study of London epidemics shortly after the Restoration. He first classified fevers (comprising two-thirds of his practice) into three main groups: continued, intermittent, and smallpox. Malaria was, of course, the typical intermittent fever. And Sydenham included measles with smallpox from which it was then occasionally difficult to differentiate. But his group of continued fevers needs a word of explanation. He believed that there was a natural period for "fermentation" in all febrile illnesses, and continued fevers included all those diseases with prolonged pyrexia. Typhus, or the fourteen day fever, was the commonest one: others were typhoid and relapsing fever. Within the recurring pattern of London epidemics, Sydenham carefully studied the natural history of these diseases (including variations in succeeding epidemics) on the simple basis of clinical observation. Then he worked out, purely empirically, the most efficacious methods of treating them. The fact that Sydenham's investigations were carried out with such thoroughness and accuracy (implying considerable experience) has lent support to the French claim, in spite of the flimsiest evidence, that he benefited from post-graduate instruction at Montpellier. Sydenham did, in fact, gain rapid clinical experience in London by supplementing the observations in his own practice with frequent visits to the sick at one of the London hospitals, probably either St. Bartholomew's or the Bridewell.[1] And later, through his friendship with Dr. Walter Needham, who became Physician to the Charterhouse in 1673, he probably also attended patients there. Sydenham acknowledged the encouragement of "the sagacious Master Walter Needham, Doctor of Medicine, an ornament both to his profession and to literature",[2] in his *Observationes Medicae* (1676).

While studying the London epidemics Sydenham set about regularizing his professional standing by sitting for a series of formal examinations leading to the licentiate of the College of Physicians. Hitherto,

[1] The evidence that he attended the sick poor at one of the London hospitals is provided by Dr. Robert Pitt who mentioned that Sydenham studied the natural history of illnesses "*in a neighbouring hospital for the meaner patients*". He was thus able to determine whether a fever could "be subdued by Natural Power [or whether] it required Bleeding, Vomitting, Purgatives, the Acid or the Aquaeous Diluters before risking the lives of people of quality", *The Antidote* (1704), p. 109.

[2] Thomas Sydenham, *Works*, ed. R. G. Latham, vol. 1, p. 5.

5. Engraving of a sketch by Hollar in 1660. View from a point about two hundred yards west of Sydenham's house in Pall Mall, looking south towards Westminster, where Sydenham's practice chiefly lay.

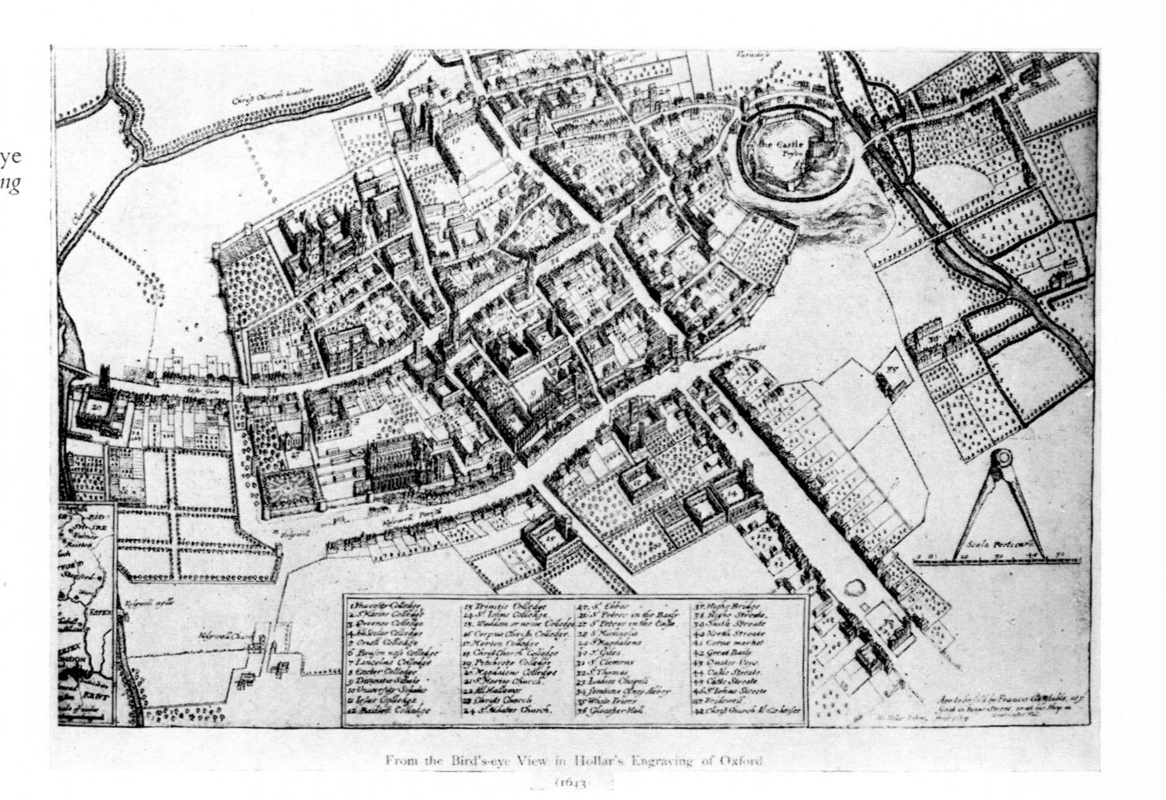

6. From the bird's-eye view in Hollar's *Engraving of Oxford*, 1643.

the regulations against unlicensed practice had not been strictly enforced, but in 1663, when Sir Edmund Alston became President he took pains to bring all doctors practising within seven miles of London into the collegiate fold. It was then that Sydenham was admitted. A year later, he moved to Pall Mall, next to the "Pestle and Mortar", the shop of his apothecary, Daniel Malthus. At the Restoration the returning nobility needed houses near the Court, and Crown lands bordering on St. James's Park were leased to them. Pall Mall, Piccadilly, the Haymarket, Soho, St. Giles, and St. Martin-in-the-Fields were rapidly populated.[1] Sydenham was one of the earliest residents in this aristocratic area, hemmed in between the swampy park and the Pimlico marshes, which doubtless provided him with a steady flow of patients with the ague. He remained there for the rest of his life.

Sydenham's clinical study of the London epidemics was rudely interrupted in the summer of 1665 when the Great Plague struck the City with volcanic fury. In July Westminster was almost deserted as the disease reached "his own door", and Hooke informed Boyle that the meetings of the Royal Society had been adjourned as the Plague "rages much about the end of the town you left. I hear several in the Pall-Mall are infected, and one house almost emptied."[2] Sydenham prudently sought safety in the country. He has been reproached for joining the vast majority of physicians who left the capital when the sick were so desperately in need of their services. But it would have been foolhardy to have remained with a wife and young family in a plague-ridden area, which was, in any case, depopulated, as the residents on whom his livelihood depended had long since departed to more salubrious areas.

Sydenham's enforced absence from practice gave him an opportunity of examining the fantastic claims of Valentine Greatraks[3] who cured patients by stroking them. Greatraks's healing mission arose from a delusion, although this should not detract from his achievements, nor diminish the power of suggestion on which they were based. Some years previously Greatraks had heard a "voice" telling him that his right arm would go dead, but he would be able to recover its use by stroking it with his left hand. The fulfilment of this prophecy intoxicated him with ideas of curing others. For three years he treated patients with the King's Evil by the laying on of hands, and his many successes led to an invitation to treat Lady Anne Conway.

[1] Mackenzie E. C. Walcott, *Handbook for the Parish of St. James Westminster* (1850), p. 41.
[2] Robert Boyle, *Works* (1772), ed. T. Birch, vol. VI, p. 501, 8 July, 1665.
[3] His cures have been studied in detail by Richard A. Hunter and Ida MacAlpine in "Valentine Greatraks", *St. Bart's Hosp. J.* (1956), **60**, 361–8.

Although Greatraks failed to relieve her intractable headaches,[1] his fame had already reached London whither he was summoned by royal command. There he treated Sir John Denham, the poet, who went "stark mad" soon after being stroked, "occasioned (as is said by some) by the rough striking of Greatrakes upon his limbs; for they said that formerly having taken the fluxing pills in Holland, and they not working, they rubbed his shins with mercury . . . it loadged in the nerves till the harsh strokes caused it to sublimate."[2] His ministrations did, however, meet with dramatic success at St. Bartholomew's Hospital.

The *virtuosi* have been daily with me since I writ to your Honor last [he wrote to Lord Conway],[3] and have given me large and full testimonials, and God has been pleased to do wonderful things in their sight, so that they are my hearty and good friends, and have stopt the mouths of the Court, where the sober party are now most of them believers and my champions. The Kings doctors this day (for the confirmation of their Majesties belief) sent three out of the hospital to me, who came on crutches and blessed be God, they all went home well, to the admiration of all people as well as the doctors.

Sydenham, who had witnessed these cures, immediately urged Oldenburg to communicate his enthusiasm to Boyle. The latter remained unimpressed. "I finde, Sir, by your silence, that you are not satisfied with the testimonials hitherto given of the Irish healer," wrote Oldenburg. "Dr. Beale and Dr. Sydenham jump in a full assurance of the truth of the thing, and the latter of them saith, that for all he brought as much prejudice against it as any man could, yet now he hath no more reason to doubt it, than to doubt whether he is a man, or some other animal."[4] Dr. Beale then enclosed two accounts of the "cures", one written by Sydenham, who "promiseth to overwhelm us with clear evidence of such wonders, as would be incredible, if not so well confirmed".[5]

After the Plague came the Great Fire of London, and in the aftermath of its devastation Sydenham's further activities are reflected in the correspondence between Boyle and his sister, Lady Ranelagh, who had been Sydenham's neighbour since 1662. Through her brother's acquaintance with Benjamin Worsley,[6] an official of the Council of Trade, she became the intermediary in a series of involved negotiations

[1] Probably due to migraine.
[2] *Conway Letters* (1930), ed. M. H. Nicolson, p. 252.
[3] *Ibid.*, p. 272, 12 April, 1666.
[4] Robert Boyle, *op. cit.*, vol. VI, p. 195, 18 September, 1665.
[5] *Ibid.*, p. 390, 7 September, 1665.
[6] An outline of Worsley's chequered career is to be found in *Notes and Queries* (1943), **185**, 123.

for financing the commercial cultivation of senna.[1] Having received some seeds from Barbados, Worsley gained Royal approval after presenting them to the King, who received the sample "not only pleasedly, but greedily". Through Lady Ranelagh he then tried to get Boyle's powerful influence and financial support. Worsley suggested that some deeds, in Boyle's name, be handed to Sydenham as security for the loan of £250 for six months.[2] These negotiations were particularly delicate as Worsley felt that he could not put any proposals before Sydenham who clearly disliked him. At the same time Lady Ranelagh had also fallen from Sydenham's favour: "(Why I no more know, than I did how I came into it) that he has not since my return home, nor for a good while before made me so much as a civil visit."[3]

Henry Oldenburg, the German-born Secretary of the Royal Society, after his imprisonment in the Tower on a charge of having "dangerous designs and practises", also complained of Sydenham's changed attitude. During his imprisonment, Oldenburg had come "to know [his] real friends". And when he was released, he refused to meet Sydenham, whom he regarded as his principal detractor.

> I must beg your excuse for not seeing Dr. Sydenham [wrote Oldenburg[4] to Boyle], who hath been the only man that I hear of, who, when I was shut up, thought fit (God knows without cause) to rail against me, and that was such a coward, as afterwards to disown it, though undeniable. I confess, that with so mean and unmoral a spirit I cannot well associate.

Sydenham's enforced absence from the metropolis during the Plague gave him an opportunity of completing his five-year study of the London epidemics published as *Methodus Curandi Febres*, etc. (1666). He dedicated this small volume of seventeen thousand words to the Honourable Robert Boyle who had verified its "truth and efficacy" as he had "gone so far as to accompany me in the visiting of the sick".[5] The book was lengthily reviewed (probably by Hooke) in the *Philosophical Transactions*[6] wherein he gave an accurate, expository, and quite uncritical summary. This practical work on the treatment of fevers enhanced Sydenham's reputation in more discerning medical circles. It came into the hands of John Locke, then an Oxford classical don,

[1] Further information on the senna project is to be found in the *Calendar of State Papers* (*America and West Indies, 1661–1668*). Worsley eventually perfected the cultivation of senna, as a licence to plant, dress, and cure it in the American plantations was granted to him for fourteen years.

[2] Robert Boyle, *op. cit.*, vol. VI, pp. 528–9, 12 September, 1666.

[3] *Ibid.*, pp. 529–30, 18 September, 1666. I am particularly indebted to Dr. R. E. W. Maddison for information about Worsley and his senna scheme.

[4] *Ibid.*, pp. 258–9, 24 December, 1667.

[5] Thomas Sydenham, *op. cit.*, vol. I, p. 10.

[6] *Philosophical Transactions* (1665–6), I, 210–13, 7 May, 1666.

though a serious student of medicine, whose notebooks[1] contain many extracts from it. And some months later, when Locke came to London as physician to Lord Ashley (later the first Earl of Shaftesbury) he lost no time in making Sydenham's acquaintance through their common friend Dr. John Mapletoft.

Hitherto, under Boyle's general direction, Locke had developed a strong iatrochemical bias, and although he had a wide theoretical knowledge of medicine, he still lacked clinical experience. At Oxford, Locke had assisted Richard Lower's physiological experiments; he had attended the medical lectures of Thomas Willis; and, at Boyle's suggestion, had prepared chemical remedies in a laboratory shared with Dr. David Thomas. Sydenham soon caused Locke to change the direction of his medical interests: henceforth, he spent less time in the chemical laboratory, and accompanied Sydenham on visits to the sick instead. "I perceive my friend, Mr. Locke," wrote Sydenham[2] to Boyle in April 1668, "have troubled you with an account of my practice, as he hath done himself in visiting with me very many of my variolous patients especially."

Locke was so impressed with his clinical visits that he wrote a Latin poem in praise of Sydenham's methods of treatment prefixed to the second edition (1668) of his book.[3] On the Continent Sydenham's book on the treatment of fevers was well received, and a cheap Amsterdam edition diffused his ideas still further. But at home his unorthodox views on the aetiology of smallpox, and his forthright criticism of other physicians, provoked some professional antagonism, which he mentioned to Boyle.

> I have the happiness of curing my patients [wrote Sydenham],[4] at least of having it said concerning me that few miscarry under me; but I cannot brag of my correspondency with some others of my faculty, who, notwithstanding my profoundness in palmistry and chemistry, impeach me of great insufficiency as I shall likewise do my taylor, when he makes my doublet like a hop-sack, and not before, let him adhere to what hypothesis he will.

Unfortunately, the efficacy of his treatment caused Sydenham to postulate a completely erroneous hypothesis on the aetiology of smallpox. He regarded the disease as a natural process which everyone

[1] B.L., MS. Locke, f. 20 *and* d. 11; B.M., Add. MS. 32554.

[2] Robert Boyle, *op. cit.*, vol. VI, pp. 648–9.

[3] Locke and Sydenham were most intimately associated between 1667 and 1672, and these entries in Locke's memoranda book (1672) reveal some of their activities: "Dr. Sydenham. Lent him 9 Jul. 70 More's 'Mystery of godliness and Mystery of iniquity' 2 folios. Dr. Mapletoft. Lent him 26 Nov. 70 'Sylvi Disputations'. Dr. Sydenham 7 March lent his treatise of feavers. Given Dr. Sydenham 13 Dec. 2 guinnys." (B.L., MS. Locke, f. 48.)

[4] Robert Boyle, *op. cit.*, vol. VI, p. 649.

had to experience at least once in his lifetime. This deduction demonstrates the universality of smallpox in his day, when Sydenham regarded it as "the most slight and safe of all other diseases". He believed that variolous blood acquired a new texture (rather like the process of moulting) which he explained in terms of physiological renewal of the blood rather than accept the current theory of vascular malignity. These views brought forth the formidable criticisms of Dr. Henry Stubbe of Warwick, a champion of ancient learning, who was then vigorously campaigning against the Royal Society, and Baconian trends in general. Stubbe had little difficulty in ridiculing Sydenham's theory, and sarcastically inquired whether "Dr. Sydenham intends to ascribe sense, appetite and judgement unto the blood."[1] He also challenged him to demonstrate any alteration in the patient's blood before or after smallpox.

Patients with smallpox were then kept warm, and given heating cordials for the purpose of driving out the elements of the disease contained within the pustules. This was the orthodox treatment. Sydenham, on the other hand, limited his efforts to aiding a natural process by bringing about separation and expulsion of variolous matter at the right time, and in the proper degree. Hence, he adopted a more moderate, and less heating, regimen. He recommended that patients should be kept out of bed for as long as possible; and afterwards covered with only the usual number of bedclothes. By bluntly stating that the high mortality of smallpox was due to the meddlesome interference of physicians and nurses favouring a hot regimen, Sydenham reaped Stubbe's most severe rebukes. "'Tis not the violence of the Disease," retorted Stubbe,[2] "but the ignorance of the Attendants which occasioned that: which is intolerable for any man to say, and refuted by Experience." And there was much truth in Stubbe's further accusation that Sydenham endeavoured "to insinuate his principles every where, with a derogation from the authorised practise of Physicians, it must needs seem that all who do not take his course have neither regard to the Patient, nor considered seriously the rise and progress of the disease". Although Sydenham's treatment of smallpox was less lethal than that of his orthodox colleagues, his theory of the disease was as wild as his criticisms were unwarranted. Stubbe clearly got the better of the argument as Sydenham wisely discarded his "moulting" theory in his later writings. But he reaped some professional antagonism as a consequence of this controversy. Other contemporary evidence showing that he continued to criticize other doctors must have provoked

[1] Henry Stubbe, *An Epistolary Discourse Concerning Phlebotomy* (1671), p. 178.
[2] *Ibid.*, p. 184.

further hostility. "Sydenham and some others in London," wrote John Ward,[1] "say of Dr. Willis that hee is an ingenious man but not a good physitian, and that hee does not understand the way of practice."

After the publication of his book on fevers, Sydenham had three other works in mind. He informed Boyle that he intended spending a "little money and time" in searching for specific medicines. Nothing came of his efforts; but two fragments of an uncompleted book, *De Arte Medica* (1668/9), have been preserved. Herein, Sydenham intended to show that clinical experience was of greater importance in the physician's main task of treating the sick than experimenting in such basic sciences as anatomy, chemistry, and botany. News of his opposition to these currently popular researches came to the notice of Dr. John Beale. When discussing with Boyle the medical value of a sound knowledge of botany, he referred to Sydenham as "a very heretic", who "detracts as much from the worth of their knowledge as they overspoke it, who gave them a godhead". He continued: "And *Hortus Sanitatis* is less faulty in overnumbering their virtues, than he in diminishing the account."[2]

Sydenham fully intended to publish a separate treatise on smallpox dedicated to Lord Shaftesbury. Further experience had confirmed his opinion that patients fared better when subjected to a downright cooling regimen. Although this work was never completed, he incorporated most of his observations into his later writings.

Locke and Mapletoft had encouraged Sydenham's researches, and he had used their secretarial abilities to get his notions on paper. They were then physicians to two of London's most patrician families: Locke lived at Lord Shaftesbury's Exeter House while Mapletoft resided with the Percys at near-by Northumberland House. As they had other duties they both sought Sydenham's advice whenever they were presented with difficult clinical problems. Thus, while the younger men virtually served a clinical apprenticeship, they, in return, encouraged Sydenham's researches, disseminated his ideas, and helped to get his views in print. Fortunately, one of Locke's manuscript notebooks,[3] containing case reports of some of the patients he treated at Exeter House in association with Sydenham, has come down to us. These detailed histories of such diverse complaints as dropsy, ague, rheumatism, lichen, hysteria, gonorrhoea, bronchitis, and pleurisy reveal Locke's sound medical knowledge before he had even bothered to take a medical degree. Here

[1] "The Reverend John Ward and Medicine", ed. Sir D'Arcy Power, *Trans. Med. Soc. Lond.* (1920), **43**, 273.

[2] Robert Boyle, *op. cit.*, vol. VI, p. 391, 11 October, 1665.

[3] B.M., Add. MS. 5714, published by E. T. Withington, *Janus* (1899), **4**, 393, 457, 527, 579; and *Med. Mag.* (1898), **7**, 47, 375, 573.

Farther observations of [illegible]

Variola

22

(1) of ye body pustles on ye [illegible] whereof many are very deepe shining red something tending to purple

Since the writing the foregoing discourse of ye small pox I have farther observed that in a flux pox ye patient begins to spit about ye 5th d. his face begins to swell 6. to be blind 7. & likewise yt when ye pustles are at their height those on ye hands & legs are larger but less proportionally as they are placed nearer the trunck & those on ye brest back & belly being very little wch also about 14 d are most gone when at ye same time those on ye hands & legs stand up high full & of a white colour, about 16 or 18 d ye patients legs begin to swell wch yet will sink agn after purging.

I have likewise met with a sort of flux pox never before by me seen. They came forth about ye 2d d with an generall uniforme red swelling all over ye face, [illegible] an erysipelas without ye least distinction of any apparent pimples at all. In ye other parts [illegible] & besides those here & there between them, especially upon the thighs, blisters, whereof some are as big as walnuts filld with thin water wch breaking the skin runs out & leaves ye flesh under it mortified. In ye progresse of ye disease a white shining skin comes on upon ye red swelling in severall parts of ye face in large patches as if it had a tendency to incrustacion all over, some parts of ye face nevertheless remaining still red. This white skin in a little while gives up a glary crusty matter, wch is not as in ye other sorts of small pox either yellow or russet but of a deeper red colour not unlike congealed dry blood wch every day grows darker till it comes at last to a perfect black. I have seene tryall both of hot & cold keepeing in this species but neither of them have succeeded though yet I finde by how much ye colder they are kept by so much they are the securer from mortifications & I am apt to believe that bleeding joyned with moderate keeping would doe well

written 14° Feb. 69/70

7. A fragment of Sydenham's treatise on smallpox in Locke's handwriting (B.L., MS. Locke, c. 29, f. 22). (*By kind permission of Bodley's Librarian.*)

are some of his notes on the treatment of Sydenham's son, William, who was suffering from measles:

Measles. March 7th, 1670. W. Sydenham, a boy aged 11 years, of a delicate constitution, with lungs naturally weak and very liable to cough, was taken with a shivering and rigor followed by a slightly raised temperature, defluxion, somnolence, cough, anorexia. The rigor, shivering and all the above symptoms, increased daily until the 5th day. The tongue on the 4th day was very white and dry. Bowels natural, but the fever increased, the respiration was difficult, more frequent than usual, and there was vomiting.

On the evening of the 5th day there appeared on the forehead and cheeks small red spots like flea bites, and all the other symptoms, especially somnolence, increased.

6th day. The whole face was discoloured by red spots of irregular shape, composed of very minute red papules, slightly raised above the surface and causing a roughness of the face perceptible to touch. The whole body was invaded by a number of similar spots, temperature raised, pulse very quick, cough with excretion of mucus brought up with difficulty. Severe dyspnoea, eyes sensitive and running, lips swollen, complete anorexia, tongue white and dry, thirst moderate, two motions.

Further notes of his illness, which lasted for fourteen days, show that Sydenham treated his son with a cooling regimen: he was allowed out of bed, and given plenty of barley water.

Sydenham's opinion was also sought during Lord Shaftesbury's prolonged illness. From the age of eighteen Shaftesbury had been troubled with recurrent abdominal pain, jaundice, and a fluctuating swelling below the right costal margin, thought to be due to a malformation of the liver rather than to a neoplasm on account of its chronicity.[1] In May 1668, after a severe attack of pain and vomiting he consulted Francis Glisson, Physician to Charles II. He was seriously ill. Pepys called his complaint an "imposthume in his breast", but many years later Osler[2] rightly diagnosed it as a suppurating hydatid abscess of the liver. Glisson recommended a purge, which intensified the pain and caused a soft tumour, the size of an ostrich egg, to appear below the costal margin. A conference of doctors concluded that an operation was necessary; and on 12 June, when a surgeon cauterized the tumour, "a large quantity of purulent matter, many baggs and skins, came away". Cysts and purulent matter continued to exude through the wound which was kept open with a wax candle. Ashley made a slow recovery. The wound was irrigated daily through a silver drainage pipe.

[1] *Memoirs, Letters and Speeches of Anthony Ashley Cooper . . . Lord Chancellor* (1859), ed. W. D. Christie, p. 32.

[2] Sir William Osler, *An Alabama Student and Other Biographical Essays* (1926). Reprinted from a special issue of *Lancet*, 1900, **ii**, 10, entitled "John Locke as a Physician".

He was much better by the beginning of September and, with Locke's assistance, drew up a questionnaire designed to get the opinions of leading physicians as to whether the drainage tube should be left in place. Sydenham's advice was sought. Along with three Royal Physicians, Glisson, Micklethwaite, and Sir George Ent, he favoured leaving it *in situ*. Shaftesbury recovered, but wore the silver pipe for the rest of his life, thereby provoking satirical comments and poems from his political opponents. He was nicknamed "Tapski", and a wine vessel fitted with a turncock was called a "Shaftesbury". A satire by Carryl, entitled *The Hippocrite*, concludes:

> The silver pipe is no sufficient drain
> For the corruption of this little man.

And of Shaftesbury Duke[1] wrote:

> The working ferment of his active mind
> In his weak body's cask with pain confined
> Would burst the rotten vessel where 'tis bent
> But that 'tis tapt to give the treason vent.

In *Albion and Albanius* Dryden described an apparition appearing before Lady Gray saying: "Bid Lord Shaftesbury have a care of his spigot; if he is tapt all the plot will run out."

Lady Dorothy Ashley Cooper (Shaftesbury's daughter-in-law) was also attended by Sydenham and Locke during her pregnancy. She had suffered one serious abortion, and another mishap was narrowly averted six months later. Locke gives these details of her illness:[2]

August 19th, 1670. Lady Dorothy Ashley, aged [blank in MS.] years, of sanguine temperament and rather phlethoric habit, noticed on the morning of the 19th (being at the end of the 12th week after conception) a sudden swelling of the abdomen without any pain, sickness, or other bodily derangement.

20th: In the evening she felt a sudden and copious flow of liquid blood from the pudenda without any pain. The flow ceased of itself, but recurred to a slight extent from time to time. She was at once bled, and two hours afterwards passed, without pain, some thin membrane with some flesh-like substance or parenchyma adhering to it, apparently part of the secundines. During the night there was neither pain nor bleeding and no sinking of the breasts or abdomen. By the physician's advice nothing was done,[3] but everything left to nature till the 23rd. No further bleeding having occurred, in order to strengthen the

[1] Quoted in R. Anderson, *A complete edition of the poets of Great Britain* (1792), vol. VI, I, 628.

[2] B.M., Add. MS. 5714, and Withington, *op. cit.*

[3] Sydenham was an exponent of expectant treatment when meddlesome interference was more common.

uterus and foetus, there was prescribed extract of acorns, 8 ozs. to be taken twice a day.

Through her physicians' care Shaftesbury's hopes of posterity were fulfilled in the birth of a grandson on 12 February, 1670/1. A few years later, when Locke's other duties began to take up too much of his time, he handed over the bulk of his practice to Sydenham, as in 1673, an apothecaries' bill for £31 12*s.* 6*d.* was for medicines mostly compounded "by Dr. Sydenham's order".[1]

While continuing his study of the London epidemics, Sydenham gained two staunch medical supporters. Dr. David Thomas of Salisbury, who had been Locke's friend since their Oxford days, often asked for his advice.[2] "Pray let me know", he wrote[3] in October 1668, "whether the grypeing of the gutts of which soe many dy in London and are sicke in the Country, be Cholera morbus, and what way of cure Sydnam useth." Occasionally Sydenham visited Salisbury in medical consultation. "Last year I was called to Salisbury", wrote Sydenham[4] in 1676, "to consult with my learned and dear friend, Dr. Thomas, upon the case of a lady whose faculties were seriously impaired. Although she was pregnant I used the above-mentioned remedies, and she recovered altogether."

Sydenham's other loyal colleague, Charles Goodall (1642–1712), was ten years younger than Locke, and eighteen years Sydenham's junior. He studied first at Cambridge, where in 1665 he was licensed to practise surgery, and on 21 June, 1670, "entered on the physic line at Leyden",[5] graduating Doctor of Medicine a month later with a treatise on scurvy dedicated to Richard Lower. After attending the anatomical lectures of Dr. Walter Needham, he served a clinical apprenticeship with Sydenham whose methods he thereafter zealously defended. Sydenham treated him like a son, and in gratitude Goodall assisted him in practice and defended his methods.

With the help and encouragement of these younger colleagues Sydenham published his most important work, *Observationes Medicae* (1676), wherein his earlier treatise on fevers was entirely recast, making it three or four times as large. In this, his main work, Sydenham extended his study of the London epidemics from 1661 to 1675. Herein he gave a more detailed description of smallpox, continued and

[1] H. R. Fox Bourne, *The Life of John Locke* (1876), vol. 1, pp. 331–2.
[2] Sydenham treated Thomas's wife and the latter sent his son to serve a clinical apprenticeship with Sydenham (B.L., MS. Locke, c. 20, f. 64).
[3] P.R.O., 30/24/47/2, ff. 27–8.
[4] Thomas Sydenham, *Works*, vol. 1, p. 94.
[5] Sir Humphrey Rolleston, "Charles Goodall, M.D., F.R.C.P. (1642–1712)", *Ann. Hist. Med.* (1940), 3rd ser., **2**, 1–9.

intermittent fevers; there were sections on acute diseases such as pleurisy, pneumonia, erysipelas, rheumatism, and quinsy, which he regarded as fevers rather than localized febrile conditions. He repeated his attacks on those physicians who treated smallpox with a heating regimen. "By such means", wrote Sydenham, "greater slaughters are committed and more havocke made of mankinde every yeare than hath bin made in any age by the sword of the fiercest and most bloody tyrant that the world ever produced." This was no exaggeration. In 1667, 1,196 died of smallpox in London, and 1,468 in the following year when the total population was only 500,000.[1] Sydenham's treatment was really quite simple. He believed that the natural time for the eruption to appear was four days after the onset of fever, and he kept the patient out of bed until then. Afterwards he allowed liberal fluids, particularly small beer, a few bedclothes, and in the case of youths, bleeding. His treatment varied slightly according to the type of smallpox, the age and constitution of the patient. But the true merit of Sydenham's methods was not so much his therapeutic innovations, as the fact that he attempted to study the natural history of fevers by simple accurate observation: in so doing he put aside many previously published theories which, he says, "have as much to do with treating sick men as the painting of pictures had to do with the sailing of ships". The work was dedicated to Dr. John Mapletoft who had translated Sydenham's English into Latin. Drs. Needham, Coxe, and Goodall are favourably mentioned; and of Locke he had this to say:[2]

You know also how thoroughly an intimate and common friend, and one who has closely and exhaustively examined the question, agrees with me as to the method I am speaking of; a man who, in the acuteness of his intellect, in the steadiness of his judgement, and in the simplicity (and by *simplicity* I mean *excellence*), of his manners, has, amongst the present generation few equals and no superiors. This praise I may confidently attach to the name of John Locke.

Locke was in Montpellier when Sydenham's book came out. After Shaftesbury's fall from power in 1675, he returned to Oxford, graduated Bachelor of Medicine, and then, ostensibly for health reasons, sought the benign air of Montpellier. During his travels Locke kept in touch with Sydenham through a monthly correspondence with Mapletoft.

My service I beseech to you [wrote Locke[3] to Mapletoft], to all my friends in your walke, particularly Dr. Sydenham. The spell held till I had left Montpellier, for by all the art and industry I could use, I could not get a booke of his

[1] Charles Creighton, *A History of Epidemics in Britain* (1894), vol. II, p. 10.
[2] Thomas Sydenham, *op. cit.*, vol. I, p. 6.
[3] B.L., MS. Locke, c. 15, ff. 205–6, 28 June, 1676.

to Montpellier till the weeke after I had left it. I shall be glad to heare that it every day gains ground, though that be not always the fate of useful truth, especially at first seting out. I shall perhaps be able to give him an account what some ingenious men thinke of it here; though I imagine he is soe well satisfied with the truth in it, and the design that made him publish it that he matters not much what men thinke. And yet there is usually a very great and allowable pleasure to see the trees take and thrive in our own time, which we ourselves have planted.

Occasionally he asked Mapletoft for Sydenham's medical advice. The air of Montpellier had not relieved Locke's bronchitis as rapidly as he had hoped, and Sydenham advised him to adopt the local diet and take water with his wine. When he reached Paris, after suffering from a bout of malaria on the way, Locke again wrote to Sydenham who allayed his hypochondrial broodings by simply stating that his symptoms were "noe other than what are usuall after agues".[1] He urged him to desist from taking various medicines, recommending horse-riding and fresh air instead. "If you would but ride on horsebacke from Paris to Calis and from Dover to London, upon that and drawing in this aer your symptoms will vanishe." Sydenham also enclosed some important details on the use and dosage of quinine.

Peruvian bark had been introduced into Europe about 1665, and a year later, Sydenham recommended it in his *Methodus Curandi Febres.* But in the second edition (1668) of his book the bark seems to have fallen from favour. There are several reasons for his indecision in fully accepting Peruvian bark as a specific in fever-ridden England. It was associated with the Jesuits,[2] and its high cost led to the peddling of many bogus preparations. One fraudulent practice, discovered by Sloane, was to substitute the cheaper bark of the cherry which was given a bitter flavour by dipping it in a tincture of aloes: it was more likely to cause diarrhoea than cure malaria. In his *Observationes Medicae* (1676) Sydenham finally realized that the bark was a specific treatment for agues. Meanwhile, Richard Talbor, an apothecary, had been using it with great success as a secret remedy. In his *Pyretologia* (1672) Talbor vaguely referred to his fever cure of four secret ingredients. Although he did not possess a licence to practise he had been exhibiting the drug with such success that he was called to treat Charles II's ague after his physician, Richard Lower, had refused to give it.[3] When he recovered, the King rewarded Talbor with a knighthood: he also allowed him to practise without a college licence, his status being specially protected by

[1] B.L., MS. Locke, c. 19, f. 163, 4 January, 1677.

[2] Gideon Harvey in *The Conclave of Physicians* (1683), p. 2, referred to the drug as "The Jesuitical or Devil's Bark".

[3] For a full account of this episode see R. E. Siegel and F. N. L. Poynter, "Robert Talbor Charles II, and Cinchona", *Med. Hist.*, 1962, **6**, 82–5.

the Secretary of State. But Sydenham firmly believed that Talbor owed his financial success to adopting the bark after reading Sydenham's book. Also he was embittered at failing to profit from pioneering the use of Peruvian bark in fever-ridden England because he had openly published the details of his method of administration. Sydenham informed Locke that Talbor had made £5,000 from the secret use of quinine and added: "He was an Apothecary in Cambridge wher my booke and practices never much obteyned."[1] Locke made a note of Sydenham's remarks on quinine, and during his travels brought it to the notice of several French physicians. It was then (1678) completely unknown in France, and Dr. Magnol, a celebrated physician of Montpellier, remained unimpressed with the remedy: "he thinks he knowes [a] better thing than kina kina to cure agues," wrote Locke in his journal.[2] In 1679 Talbor was invited to France, where he increased his fortune by treating such distinguished patients as the Prince of Condé, the Dauphin, Colbert, and Cardinal de Retz. The bark soon became known as "the English remedy", and its popularity in France caused the avaricious Talbor to corner the market to the extent that Peruvian bark reached a price of £15 a pound for a time.

Through Mapletoft, Locke consulted Sydenham when called to attend the Countess of Northumberland (wife of the British Ambassador to France) who was stricken with trigeminal neuralgia.[3] After endeavouring to allay her pain with opium he asked Mapletoft to get the opinions of some of the leading London physicians. Dr. Micklethwaite, Sir Charles Scarburgh, and Dr. Dickinson all sent long letters of advice, but Locke depended most on Sydenham's instructions. Mapletoft had secretly consulted him, and in a footnote he suggested that Locke should adopt Sydenham's treatment. "If you think the name will prejudice the advice," Mapletoft added, "you may take it upon yourselfe." And on the back of the letter he wrote: "For yourselfe. Lege solus."[4] Why the secrecy? It would appear that Sydenham was not very popular in higher medical circles. And this letter substantiates his constant complaints of professional hostility: indeed in the unpublished preface to his treatise on smallpox he stated that his life had been threatened.

I should not make these reflections [he wrote],[5] how true soever, had I not been used by some of them with these greatest indignitys beyond almost the

[1] B.L., MS. Locke, c. 19, f. 166, 3 August, 1678.
[2] *Ibid.*, f. 3, f. 316, 27 October, 1678.
[3] Details of her illness have been published by Kenneth Dewhurst, "A Symposium on Trigeminal Neuralgia", *J. Hist. Med.* (1957), **12**, 21–36.
[4] B.L., MS. Locke, c. 19, f. 164, 1 December, 1677.
[5] P.R.O., 30/24/47/2, f. 55.

suffrance of a man to the endangering not only of my reputation and lively hood but even my life its self, which may well deserve to be questiond if some have reported by unallowable practices I doe soe certainly indanger and destroy my patients.

He expressed more complaints in a letter to Boyle,[1] wherein he contrasted Talbor's flourishing and unmolested practice with his own persecution. When writing to Dr. Gould, Sydenham stated that his books were based on "downright matter-of-fact" and after his death "when the scandall of my person shall be layd aside"[2] others would also come to realize the truth of his observations. Is there any truth in Sydenham's complaints? There are, in fact, only two published criticisms of him. Dr. Henry Stubbe's admonitions have already been mentioned; and a few scurrilous remarks were made by Dr. Gideon Harvey, who does not, however, mention Sydenham by name, although his references to "a trooper turned physician" and "a Western bumpkin, that pretends to Limbo children in the Small-Pox by a new method"[3] obviously refer to him. In another passage dealing with Sydenham's treatment of smallpox, Harvey referred to him as "this generalissimo" whose methods infallibly "procured an Euthanasia. Good God, how the Universities do rob the Plough!"[4] These published provocations do not justify the picture of constant persecution which Sydenham so monotonously paints. His detractors may, of course, have slandered him. And Dr. Andrew Broun mentioned that "by the whisperings of others" Sydenham had been "baulked Imployment in the Royal Family". Broun goes on to speak about "some of his collegiate Brethren and others whose indignation at length did culminate to that height that they endeavoured to banish him, as guilty of Medicinal heresie out of that illustrious Society".[5] It seems that a faction within the College of Physicians favoured withdrawing his licence on the grounds of irregular practice. The College was then torn with dissensions. Sydenham's friend and sponsor, Dr. Thomas Coxe, was expelled from the Presidency in 1683, for political reasons. Although Sydenham never referred to his service in the Parliamentary army in his writings (such delicate matters had no place in medical books published after the Restoration), his close connexion with the Puritan Revolution would, of course, be well known, and would inevitably bring him unpopularity in more orthodox circles. The fact that Sydenham was just as great a rebel in the medical sphere as he had

[1] Robert Boyle, *op. cit.*, vol. VI, pp. 648–50.
[2] B.M., Add. MS. 4376, f. 75, 10 December, 1687.
[3] Gideon Harvey, *op. cit.*, p. 8.
[4] *Ibid.*, p. 82.
[5] Andrew Broun, *op. cit.*, p. 82.

been in his youth on the battlefields of Dorset was a constant provocation to those who did not share his opinions. And his introduction of the cooling regimen in the treatment of smallpox placed him at the centre of heated controversy which provoked the hostility and ridicule of the majority of his colleagues.

> What stories of extravagancy and folly have the talk of prejudiced people brought upon me [he wrote],[1] soe much that it has been told to persons of quality that I have taken those who have had the small pox out of their beds and put them in cold water. How much some of my own faculty have fomented and increasd these reports they themselves know and with what design I leave it to their owne consciences.

Did Sydenham magnify these stories of constant persecution? He certainly had a streak of the whining canting Puritan in his nature, but I doubt whether he greatly exaggerated. Had he done so, he would not have retained the confidence and support of Boyle, Locke, Hooke, and other friends of the highest intellectual integrity. Unfortunately, he lived at a time when medical controversy had reached great heights of vituperation. And it must be conceded that his dogmatic, highly critical, and uncompromising attitude provoked considerable antagonism; the forthright peppery qualities of the cavalry officer overshadowed the more retiring characteristics of the learned bookish physician. Occasionally, he deliberately threw down the gauntlet. "It is my nature to think where others read," he boasted,[2] "to ask, less whether the world agrees with me than whether I agree with the truth; and to hold cheap the rumour and applause of the multitude." And although Sydenham himself was highly sensitive to criticism, his cantankerous manner, as we have seen, had at times annoyed Oldenburg, Lady Ranelagh, and Willis. His temper was not improved by the constant torments of gout and the stone.

Sydenham was plagued by gout before he was thirty years old, and in 1660, after a particularly severe attack, he developed the typical symptoms of renal colic. After a long walk, he developed haematuria which became habitual after walking any distance or riding over cobbled roads. Intense concentration brought on the gout.[3] These afflictions occasionally prevented him from practising for several months. The worst episode occurred early in 1677 when he was hardly able to practise at all. He convalesced for several months at Hatfield, the seat of the Earl of Salisbury. "Dr. Sydenham who hath been laid up

[1] P.R.O., 30/24/47/2, f. 55.
[2] Thomas Sydenham, *op. cit.*, vol. II, p. 122.
[3] *Ibid.*, p. 121.

with the gout about 20 weeks," wrote Mapletoft to Locke on 25 September, 1677,[1] "hath spent five or six of them at Hatfield where he still is. A letter from him yesterday tells us that he begins to find his limbs again and hopes to be with us here in a fortnight and to fall to his business again." On this occasion, he thought that he was near death. "Had I died at that time," he wrote,[2] "death would have taken me away from the bitters of this world, not from its sweets; nor should I have resisted. I was compelled, however, to keep the house for three months and then, for the sake of restoring my health, to retire to the country for a like time." He struck another melancholy note when writing to Locke in Paris: "I have bin and am still very ill of the gout, pissing of blood etc., more than a quarter of an year; and having so many distempers broaken in upon very impayred and ill body I am in dispaire of being ever well agayne, and yet I am as well content as if I were to live and be well."[3] He was much better when he wrote again, although prolonged illness had adversely affected his practice. "I am I thank God perfectly well of my pissing blood, gout, etc., and understand my trade somewhat better than when I saw you last, but am yet but a Dunse."[4]

Chronic ill-health forced Sydenham to adopt a strict daily routine. On getting up he drank a "dish or two of tea": then he went for a coach ride until noon. After a light lunch, washed down with a quarter of a pint of canary wine, he went for another ride of two or three miles "unless prevented by business". He took a draught of small beer at supper and another one in bed, as he found that fluids tended to "cool and dilute the hot and acrid juices lodged in the kidneys whereby the stone is occasioned". To prevent haematuria during his coach rides, he took a draught of small beer before setting out. He retired to bed early, especially in winter, taking eighteen drops of liquid laudanum in canary wine to allay the torments of gout, and two and a half ounces of manna dissolved in whey to relieve symptoms of the stone.[5] Indeed, it is surprising that Sydenham managed to accomplish so much clinical work and medical writings, plagued as he was by such painful afflictions, occasionally bemused by opium, and lethargic from the effects of chronic anaemia.

The success of his *Observationes Medicae* caused his friends to urge him to set forth his views on other diseases. Dr. Brady, Regius Professor of Medicine at Cambridge, asked him to publish his further observations

[1] B.L., MS. Locke, c. 15, ff. 207–8, 25 July, 1677.
[2] Thomas Sydenham, *op. cit.*, vol. II, p. 9.
[3] B.L., MS. Locke, c. 19, f. 163, 4 January, 1677.
[4] *Ibid.*, f. 166, 3 August, 1678.
[5] Sydenham's daily routine in 1680 is described in Thomas Sydenham, *op. cit.*, vol. II, pp. 223–5.

on his method of exhibiting Peruvian bark in agues together with advice on the treatment of rheumatism. At the same time Dr. Paman, Public Orator at Cambridge and Professor of Medicine at Gresham College, requested his opinion on the treatment of venereal diseases. In his *Epistles to Dr. Brady and Dr. Paman* (1679) Sydenham made an important contribution to the treatment of fevers and rheumatism, but his treatise on venereal diseases was criticized by Dr. Pieter Guenellon of Amsterdam who added that "one would often go wrong following his method".[1] Sydenham simply recommended strong purges every morning for fourteen days, followed by clysters and oral opobalsam dropped in sugar at night in the treatment of gonorrhoea.[2]

Another short treatise was published in response to the pleas of a country physician, Dr. William Cole of Worcester. Cole had not met Sydenham (although they shared a common friend in Locke) but his experience of treating variolous patients by the cooling regimen caused him to solicit Sydenham's further observations on this method. Cole also requested his guidance in the treatment of hysteria, which brought forth the most important seventeenth-century treatise on psychological medicine.[3] In his *Epistolary Dissertation to Dr. Cole* (1681/2) Sydenham recognized that psychological illnesses were widespread. He independently confirmed Carolus Piso's earlier observation that males were also susceptible to psychological symptoms of an hysterical nature. Hitherto, this condition had been explained as "uterine suffocation" caused by corrupt menstruation—a view which Sydenham discarded. He suggested, instead, an imbalance of the "animal spirits," which, after upsetting mind-body relationship, brought on further disorders of the weakest and most vulnerable organs. He believed that those organs concerned in the purification of blood were particularly susceptible to the accumulation of putrid humours. Sydenham illustrated his opinions with clinical examples of the protean symptomatology of hysteria, similar to those described in modern textbooks. But his clinical picture differs from modern ones as he also included patients with symptoms of hypochondriasis and depression. Such complaints as deep despair and gloomy presentiments; morbid dreams and heightened suspicion; marked irritability, morbid jealousy, and insomnia would now be regarded as symptoms of manic-depressive psychosis or hypochondriasis rather than hysteria. Sydenham did, in fact, liken hypochondriasis in men and hysteria in women as "one egg as to

[1] B.L., MS. Locke, c. 11, ff. 49–52, 3/13 August, 1692.
[2] Thomas Sydenham, *op. cit.*, vol. II, pp. 38–43.
[3] Sydenham's writings on psychological medicine have been fully reviewed by Ilza Veith, *Bull. Hist. Med.* (1956), **30**, 233–40, and Jerome M. Schneck, *Amer. J. Psych.* (1957), **113**, 1034–6.

another". Within this broad classification of symptoms he found diuresis to be the commonest female complaint, whereas hypochondriacal broodings predominated in males. Bleeding and purging were recommended to purify the blood: then he exhibited fortifying remedies to reverse the morbid processes. But Sydenham's treatment was never rigid or dogmatic: sometimes he omitted medication altogether, simply leaving the patient to the care of "the prince and pattern of physicians—Time".

In 1683 Sydenham's *Tractatus de Podagra et Hydrope* came out at the bidding of Dr. Thomas Short, who had inherited Richard Lower's extensive practice when the latter lost the confidence of the Court on account of his Whig politics. This treatise on the gout is a classic. Herein Sydenham stated that the concentration required in writing it frequently brought on attacks of gout; and a coarse tremor of his hand caused him to enlist the secretarial aid of John Drake of Christ's College, Cambridge. Sydenham's remarks on dropsy were, however, much less satisfactory. Completely ignorant of the physiological and pathological mechanism causing oedema he postulated that it arose from a watery state of the blood.

Sydenham's last publication, *Schedula Monitoria de Novae Febris Ingressu* (1685), was dedicated to Dr. Charles Goodall with profuse expressions of gratitude. As Mapletoft had now forsaken medicine for the Church, and Locke was a political exile in Holland, Goodall had replaced them as Sydenham's closest medical colleague.

Sydenham had now become too feeble to do much more than advise,[1] and Goodall was gradually taking over more of his practice. In his *The College of Physicians Vindicated* (1676), Goodall had proclaimed the truth of Sydenham's methods, and the latter now returned the compliment. He described Goodall as one who "defended me with the zeal and affection of a son towards a father", which aptly expressed their relationship. This "new fever" cannot definitely be identified, but the clinical description resembles typhoid. Sydenham's last treatise is now remembered for his description of St. Vitus' Dance, or the type of chorea which still bears his name.

Some of Sydenham's lifelong friends, who had been his house pupils, reached great eminence. Sydenham practised what he preached. Having criticized university teaching as being too theoretical, he adopted instead an apprenticeship system in rounding off the training of young doctors. Sir Hans Sloane, who eventually presided over both the College of Physicians and the Royal Society, was one of his most

[1] In 1681, when only fifty-seven, Sydenham's health was so seriously shattered that he ceased to go beyond his own house for company (Thomas Sydenham, *op. cit.*, vol. II, p. 56).

renowned pupils. After qualifying at the University of Orange, Sloane handed Sydenham an introductory letter recommending him as "a ripe scholar, a good botanist, a skilful anatomist". Whereupon Sydenham, assuming his most severe military manner, is alleged to have remarked:[1]

> This is all very fine, but it won't do—anatomy, botany. Nonsense, Sir! I know an old woman in Covent Garden who understands botany better, and as for anatomy, my butcher can dissect a joint full as well. No, young man, all this is stuff: you must go to the bedside, it is there alone you can learn disease.

After this initial setback, they became firm friends, and frequently went on coach rides together. When returning from Acton, on one occasion, Sloane asked Sydenham's opinion about his proposed journey to the West Indies as Physician to the Duke of Albemarle for the purpose of studying exotic plants. Sydenham remained silent until the coach reached Green Park, where Sloane alighted. Then he retorted: "No, you must not go to Jamaica; you had better drown yourself in Rosamund's Pond[2] as you go home."[3] But Sloane did make this "suicidal" journey, and his researches into the island's flora produced a botanical classic.

Thomas Dover, who later sailed round the world on a famous privateering voyage, was one of Sydenham's pupils at the same time as Sloane. Many years later, Dover wrote a popular medical book, *The Ancient Physician's Legacy* (1732), wherein he published details of the powder which still bears his name. He also extolled Sydenham's methods, particularly his cooling treatment of smallpox, which had saved his own life when he caught the disease while serving his clinical apprenticeship.

> In the beginning I lost 22 ozs. of blood [wrote Dover].[4] He gave me a vomit, but I find by experience a purging much better. I went abroad by his direction till I was blind, and then took to my bed. I had no fire allowed in my room, my windows were constantly open, my bedclothes were ordered to be laid no higher than my waist. He made me take 12 bottles of small beer acidulated with spirits of vitriol every 24 hours. . . . I had of this Anomalous kind to a very great degree yet never lost my senses one moment.

In his own practice Dover adopted an even more drastic cooling treatment, and thereby incurred the ridicule and hostility of his colleagues.

[1] William Wadd, *Mems, Maxims, and Memoirs* (1827), p. 231.
[2] Then a common place for suicides.
[3] William Wadd, *op. cit.*, p. 232.
[4] Thomas Dover, *The Ancient Physician's Legacy* (6th ed., 1742), p. 119.

Richard Blackmore was another pupil of some distinction. Knighted by Queen Anne, Blackmore gained a minor reputation as a poet and physician. But it is unlikely that Sydenham, former cavalry officer and highly practical physician, had much in common with the bookish Blackmore, who early gave him an opportunity of showing his contempt for medical theorists. "When one Day I asked him to advise me what Books I should read to qualify me for Practice," wrote Blackmore,[1] "he replied, Read *Don Quixot*, it is a very good Book, I read it still."

Sydenham's appearance is preserved for us by the mother of another pupil, Bartholomew Beale. Mary Beale's portrait shows a man of robust frame, with long hair parted in the middle, a frank face with kindly, humorous eyes and a full and strong chin. The Puritan simplicity of his attire accentuated the quiet dignity of his bearing. His features mirrored his personality. Independence and the repudiation of dogmatic authority were his most striking characteristics. Trained in the school of revolt, Sydenham had little regard for theory or tradition, although he did possess the faculty of synthesis which enabled him to combine clinical observations into accurate pictures of disease. In his clinical work he disregarded the contributions of the natural scientists, several of the most eminent of whom were his closest friends. Most of them as well as being distinguished Fellows of the Royal Society were former Parliamentarians or, in the case of his younger colleagues, supporters of Shaftesbury's "Country Party". This is also true of many of his patients, although I doubt whether his practice was really as unremunerative as he suggested. "Wherefore were she one of those poor people whom my lott engages me to attend," he informed Locke,[2] "(for I cure not the rich till my being in the grave makes me an Authority) I would take the following course. . . ." Sydenham's own writings, and Locke's notebooks, show that he did, in fact, attend several members of the aristocracy. Through Locke and Mapletoft, he had treated the households of Lords Shaftesbury and Northumberland: he was a close friend of the Earl of Salisbury whom he also attended professionally. He mentioned treating Lord Salisbury to Locke who entered these details in his journal on 31 August, 1680:[3] "Dr. Sydenham told me he curd the E. of Salisbury of a totall supression of urine by giving him a quieting medicine at night and purgeing him the next day. For it was from a disorder of the spirits. Bleeding would have been good too but he has an abhorrency of it." And in the summer of 1683, Sydenham attended him for the last time for a "fever on his spirits".

[1] Richard Blackmore, *A Treatise upon the Smallpox* (1723), p. xi.
[2] B.L., MS. Locke, c. 19, f. 164, 1 December, 1677.
[3] *Ibid.*, f. 4, p. 165.

> Dr. Sydenham was his physician [wrote Mrs. Hill], and Mr. Stringer[1] often begged him to do all in his power to save him; and the Doctor told him if he could cure him of thinking too much of the danger the nation was in of Popery etc. he could cure his fever; but he laid that danger so much to heart, that he lost his life for it, and Mr. Stringer used to say he died a martyr for his religion and country.[2]

Sydenham also attended the Duke of Cambridge,[3] the infant son of the Duke of York, later James II, after Dr. Willis's indiscreet diagnosis of syphilis had led to his dismissal.

> There was a great phlogosis in ye Duke of Cambridge [wrote Ward],[4] his bowels. Dr. Sydenham kept ye Duke above three weeks and ye Duchess thought he would really have cured him. Hee did it by some cooling water or other wch hath got him some credit. Hee was allso with Sir Richard Bishop for his gout but did little except pultisse him with milk and crumb of bread. He advised Mr. Bishop to fast one day in a week for his rheumatismus soe as yt humour would spend ittself.

On Sunday, 6 February, 1681 Locke wrote in his journal:

> Mr. Fisher told me that Dr. Sydenham let Sir Charles Cesar bloud (which was pleuriticall) and then purged him 6 days following beginning the next day after [bleeding] for a great cough he had lately got at London, and after the purgeing by Pilulae Cochiae Majores was over he ordered him to drinke a glass of sack every night goeing to bed which [method] had succeeded well.[5]

In July 1680 Sydenham attended Lord Ossory, son of the Earl of Arlington, who was desperately ill, probably from typhoid.[6] Four other doctors, including Lower and Needham, had been treating him for several weeks. All five of them signed the last medical report which was sent to the patient's father. Lord Ossory died two days later. A post-mortem examination was performed, and it is interesting to note that this report was signed by all the doctors in attendance with the exception of Sydenham, who took the opportunity to demonstrate his disregard for morbid anatomy. Other wealthy patients mentioned in Sydenham's own writings were Lord Annesley of Belvoir Castle, Lady Anne Barrington, Mr. Thomas Wyndham, son of Sir Francis

[1] Secretary to the first Earl of Shaftesbury.

[2] W. D. Christie, *Life of Anthony Ashley Cooper, First Earl of Shaftesbury (1621–1683)*, (1871), vol. II, Appendix VIII, p. cxxix.

[3] There were three infant Dukes of Cambridge. James (1663–7) and Edgar (1667–71) were born to Anne, whilst Mary of Modena had a son on 7 November, 1677 who died on 12 December, 1677. Willis must have treated either James or Edgar as he died in 1675.

[4] D'Arcy Power, "John Ward and his Diary", *Trans. Med. Soc. Lond.* (1917), **40**, 18.

[5] B.L., MS. Locke, f. 5, p. 10.

[6] *Calendar of Manuscripts of the Marquess of Ormonde, K.P.*, Historical Manuscripts Commission (1908), n.s., vol. V, pp. 354–5.

Wyndham, and one simply referred to as "a nobleman and a friend of Lord Eliot". He treated Dr. Thomas Belke, "one of the domestic chaplains of the Earl of St. Albans"; and Dr. John Worthington, Master of Jesus College, Cambridge, during the Protectorate and later a distinguished theologian.[1] Edward Clarke,[2] a barrister and Whig Member of Parliament, was introduced to Sydenham on Locke's recommendation, as also were Mrs. Isabella Duke and her brother Sir Walter Yonge, who had been one of Shaftesbury's supporters. When asking Locke to treat her husband Mrs. Duke mentioned that he had no faith in anyone since Sydenham's death. "I cannot prevayle with him to apply himself to any Phisitian in this Country; and Sydenham being dead, he has no opinion of any in London but yourself, whose assistance he earnestly begs . . . ."[3] Several doctors, including Locke, Thomas, and Dover, were Sydenham's patients. He also mentioned treating a Dr. Morris for a continued fever, and Dr. Daniel Coxe for dysentery.

Sydenham's daily routine included frequent coach rides, usually to Acton, in the company of his friends or apprentices, and in the evenings he frequented either Jonathan's or Garway's Coffee House in the company of Boyle, Hooke, Wren, or Locke.[4] Hooke's journal gives a glimpse of his habits. On 8 June, 1675 he wrote: "Rode to Acton with Dr. Siddenham, did me good, he invited me to stay with him 6 weeks. Told me of his book. Discoursd with me of Physick, Religion, philosophy."[5] In August 1675 Hooke dined with Boyle, then called on Sydenham and walked with him to Bloomsbury; and a few months later they spent the evening together at Jonathan's Coffee House with Mapletoft and Wagstaffe.

Charles James Fox recounts a story of Sydenham taking the evening air at an open window of his house on the north side of Pall Mall, which gave an unobstructed view over St. James's Park. One evening when he was quietly smoking a pipe and enjoying a drink of beer from a silver tankard, a thief snatched the tankard and made off with it.

[1] *Diary and Correspondence of Dr. John Worthington* (1846), ed. James Crossley, vol. II, pt. 2, p. 308.

[2] On 25 November, 1686, Clarke informed Locke: "My eldest son fell ill of a violent Feaver, which in 3 or 4 days time, notwithstanding all the endeavors of Dr. Sydenham and Dr. Goodall to the contrary, gott soe into his head that he has layne ever since—this being now the 13th day since he was taken ill—in a daz'd and sleepy condition and hath taken nothing but of their prescribing." (B.L., MS. Locke, c. 6, f. 23.)

[3] *Ibid.*, c. 8, ff. 43–4, 2 March, 1690.

[4] "1657. An excellent drink called Chocolate; sold in Bishopsgate Street; also the drink called coffee. Tea began to be sold by Garway in Exchange Alley, Tobacconist and Seller and Retailer of Tea and Coffee." (Wadd, *op. cit.*, pp. 232–3.)

[5] *The Diary of Robert Hooke (1672–1680)*, ed. H. W. Robinson and W. Adams (1935), p. 163.

Locke renewed his friendship with Sydenham after his return from France in 1679, and during the next three and a half years they spent many weekends together. Locke's journal entries show that he profited from these meetings. Most entries are simply recipes recommended by Sydenham, but the occasional short case report throws more light on his practice:

Mrs. Duke of a phlegmatique and tender constitution often times conceived but in the 10th week always miscaried of a false conception. She had tried the aire and physitians of France; the waters and physitians of England for many years but all in vain. At last consulting Dr. S[ydenham] he concluded those false conceptions to proceed from want of spirits and coldnesse in the habit and womb, which he thought were to be warmed and strengthend, to which purpose he gave her 2 spoonfuls in the morning of his grand cordiall, which she has now taken these many months and haveing since conceived is now in the 8th or 9th month of her being with child. Elixir Alexipharmacum.[1]

Locke gleaned many details of the London epidemics, a knowledge of which (according to Sydenham's teaching) was an essential prelude to correct treatment.

Sat. Nov. 15. The constitution of this Autumn was intermittent and quarternary though many of the fevers in the beginning were continued and severall made soe by ill management, but might be cured of agues or intermittents, being first procured by drinking whey 2 or 3 days.

In September severall children had hooping coughs. After October noe more ordinary agues but such as returnd. In November all the world at London had violent coughs without spiting which were from hot strains irritating the lungs. Whey taken without anything else 2 or 3 days cured. Or bleeding with 3 days purging.[2]

A few days later Locke made this note on the effect of an epidemic of pneumonia on the mortality rates:

Thursd. Nov. 27. The bills of mortality this week increased 222 as that of the week before 213, in all 435 the last fortnight. It is an increase scarce ever known out of times of pestilentiall diseases. The Epidemical disease that came in at this time and caused this mortality was a dry but violent cough which produced in many a peripneumonia.

Cure with (1) bleeding, (2) blistering ointment, (3) thrice purging.[3]

Frid. Sept. 10. 1680.[4] The dysenteries of this intermittent Constitution are nothing but the fever inverted and so are curd with the cortex addeing a bridle to it.

[1] B.M., Add. MS. 15642, f. 165, 18 October, 1679.
[2] *Ibid.*, f. 203.
[3] *Ibid.*, f. 181.
[4] B.L., MS. Locke, f. 4, p. 168.

Rx. 1 drachm of Peruvian cortex powdered with alcohol (otherwise it gripes the stomach), 10 grains of saffron and some syrup of dried roses. Make a bolus. Repeat every 4th hour. This cures.

Tuesd. Nov. 16. 1680. The fever of the intermittent kinde now reigning has sometimes vomiting, great pains in the bowels and the back with red water as if there were a stone, and the Peruvian bark will not help.

[Method of Cure:] drink sack soe plentifully as to continue a little intoxicated for some days and this will soe strengthen the bloud as it will cure.[1]

Mond. Oct. 3. 1681: Fevers of this intermittent type, even if actually continuous, are cured by KinKina if the patient is not kept in bed but allowed to rise in the daytime. Continuous lying down results in a continuous fever.[2]

He also took a note on Sydenham's method of curing hysteria, using five remedies, beginning with asafoetida and discarding each one until the patient responded;[3] and his treatment of madness with a course of bleeding and purging once a week for a long period.[4] Other notes were merely terse statements based on Sydenham's long experience, such as occur in the entries for Monday, 5 September and Saturday, 10 September, 1681.[5]

Women and children scape much better in the smallpox than men.

Gonorrhoea is cured by purgeing daily for 14 days and then at greater intervals. This is Sydenham's method.

Venereal Decay, even when intricate, is cured by purging every 4th day and drinking a decoction of Sarsparilla alone. This is Dr. Clarges' method. N.B. Investigate this more fully.

Riding long journeys on horseback was one of Sydenham's favourite remedies, particularly for phthisis. By such means he cured his nephew Mr. Lawrence; and he also mentioned attending "a poor neighbour of my own", suffering from biliary colic, to whom he lent a horse from his own stable so that he could undertake the treatment.[6] Dr. Paris tells an amusing story of a deception practised by Sydenham in order to get a wealthy patient to undertake a long journey in the saddle. After attending him for several months without alleviating his symptoms, Sydenham frankly told him that he was unable to render any further service. But he added that a certain Dr. Robertson of Inverness had performed several remarkable cures in this particular malady.

[1] B.L., MS. Locke, f. 4, p. 193.
[2] *Ibid.*, f. 5, p. 131.
[3] B.M., Add. MS. 15642, p. 179, 1 December, 1679.
[4] B.L., MS. Locke, f. 4, p. 169, 10 September, 1680.
[5] *Ibid.*, f. 119.
[6] Thomas Sydenham, *op. cit.*, vol. 1, p. 197.

Armed with Sydenham's letter of introduction, the patient set out for Inverness where he lost no time in seeking Dr. Robertson. To his dismay he learned that there was no physician of that name in the city, nor had there ever been one in the memory of anyone there. Returning to London the gentleman vented his indignation on Sydenham for having sent him on such a long and fruitless journey. "Well," inquired Sydenham, "are you any better in health?"

"Yes, I am now quite well, but no thanks to you."

"No," added Sydenham, "but you may thank Dr. Robertson for curing you. I wished to send you on a journey with some objective interest in view. I knew it would be of service to you; in going you had Dr. Robertson and his wonderful cures in contemplation, and in returning, you were equally engaged in thinking of scolding me."[1]

Although this story has probably been embellished, it is, nevertheless, in keeping with the simplicity of Sydenham's therapy in which fresh air, exercise, and dietary moderation played so large a part. Sydenham illustrated the benefits of horse-riding in psychological illness when treating a clergyman for "hypochondriasis" brought on by excessive study. After all medicinal remedies had proved ineffective, he suggested daily rides of increasing duration, as much as the patient's strength would allow. He was soon undertaking long and arduous journeys:

> Indeed, like a traveller, he took no care of regular meals, nor yet of the weather. He just took them as they fell out: so he went on until he got to twenty or thirty miles a day, and finding himself, after a few days, much better, kept on for some months. Indeed, as he told me himself, he rode more than a thousand miles, by which time he had gained perfect health and vigour. Riding is as good in a decline or in phthisis as in hypochondriasis. It has cured patients whom many medicines would have benefitted as much as many words —and no more.[2]

Sydenham believed that riding was beneficial in many conditions, unless contraindicated by old age or renal calculus, when he recommended a carriage instead, "which is a blessing to gouty people; inasmuch as that very wealth which fostered the luxury which brought about the disease supplies the means of keeping a vehicle, whereby those can take the one sort of exercise when they could not take the other".[3]

"Accubitus", a method of heating devitalizing elderly patients with either a live puppy or a young person, was another of Sydenham's

[1] Quoted by J. A. Paris in *Pharmacologia* (1825), p. 48 and in John Brown, *Locke and Sydenham* (1866), pp. 87–8.

[2] Thomas Sydenham, *op. cit.*, vol. II, p. 107.

[3] *Ibid.*, p. 149.

homely remedies. He used this treatment early in his practice. In May 1662, when called to see a Mrs. Change, "very ill of a cholera morbus", he got her husband to lie naked close to her back, and her son, aged twelve, against her belly: their natural heat soon resuscitated the patient.[1] He treated a woman for dysentery by causing her son,

> a plump, hot lad of thirteen years of age, and her nurse's son of six or seven years, to go to bed to her naked and to lie the one close to her belly, the other close to her back, which they did, and so long as they continued with her she had no stools; but the boys rising at any time the looseness would immediately return. I commanded that she should persist in her course till her cure should be complete (the boys relieving one another by turns in the daytime) and so she fully recovered.[2]

This treatment was successfully applied to a man with a continued fever of such severity that his doctor "judged him a dead man" until Sydenham suggested that a link-boy should lie very close to him all night.[3] The same method was used in treating the wife of Nicholas Monk, Bishop of Hereford, sister-in-law to the Duke of Albemarle, when suffering from an ague. Sydenham arranged for a girl of thirteen to be put close to her breasts, which caused her speedy recovery. The girl then fell sick. Her illness was imputed to contact with the patient, which Sydenham confidently denied as he had never experienced a similar case. But unfortunately for his argument the girl developed petechial haemorrhages indicating that she had probably contracted septicaemia.

Sydenham's domestic life seems to have been reasonably placid. He had three sons, William, Henry, and James. His wife, mother-in-law, and the occasional medical apprentice, completed the family circle. The eldest son, William, entered Pembroke College, Cambridge, in 1674, but left without taking a degree. Eventually he qualified in medicine in Scotland, probably at Marischal College, Aberdeen, became a Licentiate of the College of Physicians in 1687, and joined his father in practice. Shortly after the publication of his *Medical Observations*, Thomas Sydenham graduated Doctor of Medicine from Pembroke College, Cambridge, the change of University probably being determined by his son's residence there. Little is known of the other two sons. Henry became a merchant in Spain, and James was still a minor at the time of his father's death in 1689.[4] He was probably short of money until he came of age, as the correspondence between Thomas and Locke shows that they helped him to get a commission

[1] Thomas Sydenham, *op. cit.*, vol. II, Appendix C, p. 371. [2] *Ibid.*
[3] *Ibid.* [4] J. F. Payne, *op. cit.*, pp. 196–9.

in the army.[1] "I wrote to Collenel Mathews in favour of Mr. Sydenham before I receaved your letter and therefore have delayed my answere so long and I am not without hope of successe. Captaine Young who is of that regiment and Mr. Sydenham's friend being ready to sollicite for him and who did acquaint Mr. Sydenham that I wrote effectually."

Sydenham was comfortably off. As a younger son he would not have inherited much from his father, and the estates in Leicestershire and Herefordshire, left to his eldest son, may have been sequestered Royalist lands. The bulk of his estate went to William, the second son, Henry, being left £200, reduced by £50 in a codicil of 29 November, 1689, as that amount had already been given him for "an adventure". James was left a similar amount to be paid two years after his father's death, and his mother-in-law, Mrs. Gee, received an annuity of £25. He also provided for his eldest brother's family by leaving £30 to James Thornhill,[2] his niece's son, in order to bind him apprentice to some trade or profession.

Towards the end of his life Sydenham's writings made him more famous abroad than at home. Ettmüller in Leipzig, Dolius in Hesse, and Spon of Lyons were some of the well-known continental doctors who honoured his name and adopted his clinical methods. And John Locke, more than any other Englishman, helped to bring Sydenham's ideas to the notice of foreign doctors during his long residence abroad. When travelling in France Locke introduced Sydenham's writing to the leading physicians; and later, when a political exile in Holland for over five years, he was his constant advocate and interpreter.[3] Several leading Dutch physicians adopted Sydenham's methods as a direct consequence of Locke's mediation, and one of them, Dr. Matthew Slade, wrote some verses in Sydenham's honour[4] and came to England specially to meet him. Locke's closest medical colleague, Dr. Pieter Guenellon, one of Amsterdam's leading physicians, used Sydenham's writings as the basis of his lectures; and his father-in-law, Dr. Egbertus Veen, praised his methods in the treatment of chronic diseases. In a letter to Locke, Veen expressed regret that he had not come across his works earlier. Dr. Caspar Sibelius was another Dutch physician, who

[1] B.L., MS. Locke, c. 20, ff. 89–90, 28 March, 1691.

[2] Sir James Thornhill (1676–1734), the painter. He was Colonel William Sydenham's grandson who decorated the interior of St. Paul's Cathedral. His daughter married artist William Hogarth.

[3] During his residence in Holland Locke probably reviewed Sydenham's *Schedula Monitoria de Novae Febris Ingressu* (1686) in the *Bibliothèque Universelle*. "Remember me to M. Le Clerc," wrote Locke, "and tell him that I have just received from England a new book of Sydenham's which I have not yet read. If he desires either the book or a review of it, I will gladly send him either." (Amsterdam, Remonstrant's MS., 10 April, 1687.)

[4] Published by Kenneth Dewhurst, *Janus* (1962), **50**, 193.

later emigrated to England, and on Locke's recommendation adopted Sydenham's writings as his clinical guide. While in Leyden, Locke befriended a young Irish medical student who eventually reached the pinnacle of his profession in Ireland. Many years later, as Sir Thomas Molyneux, President of the Dublin College of Physicians, he thanked Locke for introducing him to Sydenham's writings.[1]

> Some Years after I left you in Holland, upon my Return for *England*, I contracted no small Intimacy with *Dr. Sydenham*, on Account of having been known to you, his much esteemed Friend; and I found him so accurate an Observer of Diseases, so thoroughly skill'd in all useful Knowledge of his Profession, and withal so communicative, that his Acquaintance was a very great Advantage to me: And all this I chiefly owe to you, Sir. . . .[2]

But Locke's most important Dutch medical acquaintance was Dr. Schacht, Professor of Medicine at Leyden. He linked Sydenham with his famous successor, Dr. Herman Boerhaave, who, more than any other physician, greatly extended Sydenham's observations a generation later.

Locke survived Sydenham by fifteen years during which he did much to further the latter's posthumous fame. When Guenellon heard of Sydenham's death in 1689 he asked Locke whether "we can look forward to any posthumous works", and although Locke was unable to provide any new material, he sent him books on phthisis and children's diseases which "tried to follow the plan of Dr. Sydenham".[3] And when Goodall sought Locke's assistance in a survey in social medicine he put him in touch with various foreign physicians to whom he addressed a questionnaire. The last inquiry was concerned with "the Esteeme which Physitians have had of Dr. Sydenham and his Works".

> As regards the works of Sydenham [replied Guenellon],[4] we value them highly; his plan and method are certainly admirable. However, he has not had equal success in every direction and his remarks on gonorrhoea are very feeble, and one would often go wrong following his method.

In another letter Guenellon mentioned that Peruvian bark "has not quite the vogue it has acquired in England and France".[5]

[1] Details of Locke's activities in Holland are to be found in Kenneth Dewhurst's *John Locke, Physician and Philosopher* (1963), pp. 224–81.

[2] *Familiar Letters between Mr. John Locke and Several of his Friends* (4th ed., 1742), p. 218, 27 August, 1692.

[3] B.L., MS. Locke, c. 11, ff. 28–9, 11/21 March, 1704.

[4] *Ibid.*, ff. 49–51.

[5] *Ibid.*, ff. 51–2.

Dr. Willoughby, Registrar of the Dublin College of Physicians, sent this reply:[1]

Dr. Sydenham was undoubtedly a good observer and a faithful Register of all his observations, butt it is to be suspected that he was sometimes a little too hasty in determining the periods of those motions which did Constitute the Characteristick of the distemper, which may be observed by an indifferent practiser to vary their seasons with much more latitude then he doth allow. He has been very honest in rescinding from Physick all the unnecessary pomp of alternatives and preparatives and reducing it only to the use of Grand remidys which in Phisick doe justly fill both sides of the loafe. I can easily concur with him, in the great Admiration he has for the Jesuit's Bark and doe believe opium to be one of the greatest remedies in nature, tho' I cannot reckon it as he doth the greatest Cordiall, since to perform its effect it reduces men to an Estate more like that of death then life and in a small quantity, commands and overcomes all the power of nature, and if by accident it happen to releive some, 'tis because nature at that time needs such a mortification to reclaim its extravagant fury, and reduce it to itselfe. This I speak not as an enemy to opium, for I take more of it myselfe then some Physicians who are crowded with patients finde occation to prescribe, yett I cannot butt thinke, since it is soe indigestible, it has more of a poyson in itt then a Cordiall, and 'tis by accident, not any cordiall vertue, that it performes these surprising cures which to ignorant spectators seem to have more of magicall then naturell in them.[2]

In England, Thomas Willis's *Rational Therapeutics* was the more favoured medical textbook until long after Sydenham's death, when it was superseded by the latter's *Observationes Medicae*. However, some younger practitioners perpetuated Sydenham's fame in their writings. Richard Morton was the best known. He referred to Sydenham as a "Prince of Physicians" and concluded: "If I were able to hold forth the renown of so great a Man as our Sydenham, I should extol his name to the skies, and set him for a noble example for the most experienced Practitioner to walk by."[3] Another laudatory testimony is to be found in Dr. Walter Harris's book[4] on acute diseases in children.

There are many prolix disputations on Catharsis in fevers, most of them aiming at a display of learning. Sydenham with his unusual courage and superior intellect dealt with this matter about which others had supplied only words, backing his argument with many reasons and giving practical proof of it.

Dr. Andrew Broun of Edinburgh was so impressed with Sydenham's works that he hastened to London to make his acquaintance. "Then

[1] B.L., MS. Rawlinson, c. 406, f. 68.
[2] *Ibid.*, ff. 79–80.
[3] Richard Morton, *Opera Medica* (1697), p. ii.
[4] Walter Harris, *De Morbis Acutis Infantum* (1697), p. 19.

after some months spent in his society," returned home "as much overjoyed as I had gotten a treasure."[1] While still an Oxford undergraduate, Radcliffe boasted that he was preparing himself for medicine with a recent work of Sydenham's and other modern writers to the exclusion of the "rubbish of antiquity contained in musty volumes".[2]

What is the lasting value of Sydenham's writings? He rid the *Pharmacopoeia* of many dangerous and obnoxious remedies, and introduced several useful therapeutic innovations. His pioneering of quinine was of immense benefit in fever-ridden England, and countless lives were saved by his cooling regimen in the treatment of smallpox. He exhibited iron, either in the form of steel filings or as a syrup, in the treatment of hysteria and chlorosis; and in a pain-racked age he wisely realized the value of opium which he gave in the form of liquid laudanum, replacing the solid pill commonly used in his day. Sydenham often dispensed with drugs altogether, and prescribed such simple remedies as fresh air, exercise, a moderate diet, and the purgative waters of Barnet or Lewisham. These were bold innovations in an age when excessive doses of drugs were usually prescribed. But his reputation does not depend so much upon the many sensible and effective remedies he helped to introduce, as upon the general clinical principles which guided his own practice of medicine and illustrated his writings. Sydenham's revival of the Hippocratic method of studying the natural history of diseases by making a series of accurate and detailed observations set the clinical pattern of future progress, so aptly summarized by Locke:[3]

> I wonder, that after the Pattern Dr. *Sydenham* has set them of a better Way, Men should return again to that Romance Way of Physick. But I see it is easier and more natural for Men to build Castles in the Air of their own, than to survey well those that are to be found standing. Nicely to observe the History of Diseases, in all their Changes and Circumstances, is a work of Time, Accurateness, Attention and Judgment. . . .

It was by such means that Thomas Sydenham, rebel, soldier, and physician, laid the foundations of clinical medicine.

[1] Andrew Broun, *op. cit.*, p. 83.
[2] R. T. Gunther, *Early Science in Oxford* (1937), vol. XI, p. 82.
[3] *Familiar Letters between Mr. John Locke and Several of his Friends* (4th ed., 1742), pp. 223–4, 20 January, 1692/3.

Theoretical Influences

LIKE many practical men, Sydenham deluded himself into believing that he had completely discarded theory. Currie mentioned that although Sydenham affected not to speculate, "his theorizing was evident on every page of his book".[1] This is a gross exaggeration. Sydenham certainly aimed at studying diseases by simply recording plain matters of fact, free from preconceived hypotheses, and, to a great extent, he succeeded. But no observer of Nature can ever hope to attain this ideal and Sydenham was no exception. His writings reveal that he was influenced, in varying degrees, by Hippocrates, Bacon, and Boyle.

Sydenham took much for granted in the medical system of Hippocrates for whom he showed great respect.[2] Three aspects of Hippocratic writings particularly interested him. First, the abundance of clinical observation, rather than airy speculation, stimulated Sydenham to perfect the art of accurate clinical observation. Hippocrates simply presented case-histories, whereas Sydenham used them to build up disease-histories rather like the botanical delineation of plants. "It is necessary that all diseases be reduced to definite and certain species," wrote Sydenham,[3] "and that, with the same care which we see exhibited by botanists in their phytologies."

Secondly, he used the Hippocratic method of carefully observing the prevailing maladies of each season and year as a model for his own study of the London epidemics between 1661 and 1675. During these fourteen years, Sydenham recognized the following five periods: (1) 1661–4, (2) 1665–6, (3) 1667–9, (4) 1670–72, (5) 1673–5, each of them being characterized by a particular *epidemic constitution* or disposition of the atmosphere. It was the nature of the epidemic constitution that caused outbreaks of certain fevers. First, intermittent fevers predominated together with a peculiar species of continued fever. Then plague broke out, and was accompanied by other pestilential fevers, analogous to, but different from, the true plague. In the third, or variolous constitution, smallpox predominated, and was accompanied by another fever of the same epidemic constitution which Sydenham called variolous fever. The dysenteric constitution predominated

[1] Quoted by Thomas Young, *An Introduction to Medical Literature* (1813), pp. 51–2.

[2] Sydenham's adherence to Hippocratic principles has been summarized by J. F. Payne, *Thomas Sydenham* (1900), pp. 222–35.

[3] Thomas Sydenham, *Works* (1848), ed. R. G. Latham, vol. 1, p. 13.

during the fourth period causing cholera, summer diarrhoea, an unspecific fever resembling dysentery, an anomalous type of smallpox, and true dysentery. The fifth constitution was characterized by a comatose fever and an epidemic cough, probably influenza.

Sydenham believed that fevers changed their characteristics according to the constitution of the year, and the nature of the prevailing epidemic. If, for example, a certain type of smallpox was present, then the concomitant fever, such as measles or dysentery, could also be predicted *before* any such cases became apparent. This concept of a definite epidemic constitution in particular years echoed Hippocratic teaching. And from this supposition, Sydenham argued that certain medicines which were effective for one epidemic constitution might be ineffective in the same disease when a different epidemic constitution prevailed.

In discussing the actual causation of disease, Sydenham argued within the framework of the Hippocratic doctrine of the humours. According to this theory, diseases were thought to be due to a disturbance of the four imaginary humours or elementary principles of the body. Sydenham's adherence to the humoral doctrine has often been overlooked. Arguments based on humoral pathology appear throughout his published works, and a manuscript essay, *Of the Four Constitutions*, published here for the first time, is devoted entirely to explaining gout in terms of a humoral imbalance. Briefly, humoral theory postulated that when a morbid state causes one of the four bodily humours to be produced excessively, then the body's defences come into action as is shown by the patient's raised temperature. Thus, the humour is "cooked" and separated, with eventual evacuation of the "raw" portion. The physician could, of course, assist this process by simply warming the patient either through the use of external heat or the exhibition of sudorifics; and he could hasten evacuation by the use of purges, emetics, sudorifics, or bleeding. But treatment was much more complicated than simply exhibiting one or other mode of evacuation: its true art lay in giving the correct strength of the right medicine at appropriate intervals throughout the whole course of the illness. The duration of treatment was also of the utmost importance. When, as often happened, treatment administered by the most skilled and experienced physician failed to cure or alleviate the sickness, then it could *not* be implied that the whole hypothesis was false: the doctor had only the right to infer that the proper set of determinate values had not been rightly applied.[1] Thus, the humoral doctrine as a whole was most difficult to refute.

[1] For a more detailed discussion of Sydenham's attitude to humoral pathology, see R. M. Yost, "Sydenham's Philosophy of Science", *Osiris* (1950), 9, 84–104.

Although humoral pathology was Sydenham's general working hypothesis, he discarded it whenever he found that his own clinical experience was at variance with its tenets. He had found by experience, for example, that a cooling regimen mitigated the symptoms of small-pox, and when treating variolous patients he always put aside humoral doctrines. To his merit, Sydenham placed more reliance on empirical findings than upon humoral theory; and any doubts were settled by a final appeal to observable facts rather than to theory.

> Now if the present reasons be insufficient to prove absolutely that my view is the right one [he wrote],[1] I shall be contented with the evidence of experience. This says that fevers like the present yield very slowly to the sweating treatment; which is enough—since it is not reason but experience which teaches us what fevers are cured by diaphoresis, and what by other evacuations. As to speculative reasons, no wise man, who knows the nature of either men or things, will fail to see that there is no certain experiment by which they can be tested.

There is also some incompatibility in Sydenham's general acceptance of humoral pathology and his use of, and search for, other specific medicines, such as quinine, which had no heating, cooling, or purging action. As soon as he realized that cinchona bark was a specific remedy in intermittent fevers, Sydenham discarded humoral notions and strongly advocated its benefits to all his colleagues. According to Yost,[2] the success of his cooling regimen and his realization of the specific qualities of quinine caused Sydenham, towards the end of his life, to consider jettisoning humoral pathology as it gradually began to collapse under the weight of various *ad hoc* hypotheses thrust upon it by empirical facts.

While Hippocratic writings revealed to Sydenham the importance of building clinical foundations upon accurate case-histories, it was the works of Bacon and his disciples that gave him the idea of compiling disease-histories from these clinical records. "We have not to imagine, or to think out, but to find out what Nature does or produces"[3] is one of several quotations from Bacon scattered throughout his works. And in studying the natural history of diseases, Sydenham closely followed Baconian methods similar to those adopted by his friends of the Royal Society in their classification of animals, vegetables, and minerals. But Sydenham included only morbid signs that were macroscopically observable such as the blotchy rash of measles and the puffy swellings of dropsy. He then concluded that these recurrent generic features of a disease would probably respond to the same treatment. In this manner

[1] Thomas Sydenham, *op. cit.*, vol. II, p. 211.
[2] R. M. Yost, *op. cit.*, p. 104.
[3] Quoted on title-page of *Tractatus de Podagra et Hydrope* (1683).

he gradually developed a clinical picture of a disease-process together with its response to various forms of treatment.

> For my own part [he wrote],[1] I think we have lived thus long without an accurate history of diseases, for this especial reason; viz. that the generality have considered that disease is but a confused and disordered effort of Nature thrown down from her proper state, and defending herself in vain; so that they have classed the attempts at a just description with the attempts to wash blackamoors white.

Sydenham then tried to link his case-histories with other morbid states and with the type of environment which ushered in the illness. These correlations were then assembled into disease-histories, and whereas his case-histories were merely a series of individual records, this wider classification provided him with a clinical repository from which empirical generalizations could be drawn. He did, however, stress that disease-histories must always be tested and re-examined in the light of any subsequent observations. Sydenham was reluctant to subdivide a class of diseases unless the morbid condition could be cured, or vastly improved, by some new method of treatment.[1]

So far Sydenham's methodology is eminently Baconian: indeed his main critic, Dr. Henry Stubbe, described him as a "semi-virtuoso". And again when urging Boyle to discontinue his experimental work, which he thought was undermining religion, and established practice, Stubbe clearly regarded him as one of the supporters of the Royal Society. "I know not what any physician may, as the mode is, tell you to your face, but except it be such as Dr. Sydenham and young Coxe I believe not one lives that doth not condemn your experimental philosophy."[2] Of Sydenham's closest colleagues only Charles Goodall was not a Fellow of the Royal Society. Boyle, Locke, Needham, Sloane, Hooke, and Millington were amongst the more illustrious Fellows who were also Sydenham's closest friends. There were several others with whom he was on friendly, though less intimate, terms. Sir William Petty (1623–87), physician, political economist, and a fellow-victim of the gout, was his near neighbour in Pall Mall. Another former Parliamentarian was Dr. Jonathan Goddard (1627–79). After serving Cromwell in Ireland, Scotland, and at the Battle of Worcester, he was appointed Warden of Merton College, Oxford, and later became Professor of Physic at Gresham College. He had been a member of Cromwell's Council of State at the same time as Sydenham's brother. Goddard was also a founder-Fellow of the Royal Society, and

[1] Thomas Sydenham, *op. cit.*, vol. I, pp. 15–16.
[2] T. Birch, *op. cit.*, vol. I, p. cxv, 4 June, 1670.

a good practical chemist. Sydenham preferred his Guttae Goddardianae vel Anglicanae to all other volatile spirits for "energetically and efficaciously attainting the end, for which they are applied".[1] Of a younger generation of physician-scientists was Dr. Robert Pitt[2] (1653–1712), whose anatomical researches led to his election into the Royal Society. On moving to London Pitt became Physician to St. Bartholomew's Hospital and a Censor of the College of Physicians. Any of these men would willingly have nominated Sydenham for election into the Royal Society had he so desired. He frequently met Robert Hooke, the Society's indefatigable Curator of Experiments, at Jonathan's Coffee House. On one occasion, Hooke recorded that Sydenham "discoursd with me of Physick, Religion, philosophy";[3] and later, mentioned that he had "confounded Sydenham's novice metaphysica".[4] What were their differences? They both held that true knowledge was based on experience. "The careful observations of facts under the cognisance of our senses, and not . . . the flimsy fancies based on uncertain foundation of opinion", though proclaimed by Sydenham,[5] was, in fact, the ultimate goal of all the endeavours of these early scientists. Sydenham's differences with his scientist friends arose over the reliability of knowledge gained from different varieties of experience. Was it valid, for example, to diagnose, and subsequently treat, a patient on the basis of microscopical observations? On this issue Sydenham profoundly differed from his friends. Believing as he did that the relevance of anatomical dissections had been greatly over-esteemed in training a physician for his main task of treating the sick, he regarded attempts at transcending normal perception with the aid of microscopes as immoral and completely outside God's purpose. The physician's *duty* was simply to confine his observations to the "outer husk of things",[6] God having so shaped his faculties as to perceive only the superficies of bodies, and not the minute processes of Nature's "abyss of cause".[7] Sydenham had other objections to the use of microscopes. He argued that such observations were meaningless and would only cause further fruitless speculations completely remote from clinical realities. Sydenham also completely disregarded pathological observations made in the dead-house. He did so for therapeutic reasons. As he was mainly concerned with assessing

[1] W. Munk, *op. cit.*, vol. I, p. 202 and *D.N.B.*, vol. VIII, pp. 114–15.

[2] His career is outlined in Kenneth Dewhurst's "Dr. Robert Pitt's Letters to John Locke", *St. Bart's Hosp. J.* (1962), **11**, 258–67.

[3] *The Diary of Robert Hooke (1672–1680)* (1935), ed. H. W. Robinson and W. Adams, p. 163.

[4] *Ibid.*, p. 177.

[5] Thomas Sydenham, *op. cit.*, vol. II, p. 60.

[6] *Ibid.*, p. 171.

[7] *Ibid.*, vol. I, p. 102.

a patient's response to treatment, he considered that pathological data would tend to confuse this main aim.[1] His passionate Puritan morality clearly limited his medical research. After categorically stating that a physician's task was simply to cure disease, and "to do nought else", Sydenham then criticized doctors who put their trust in speculative theories.

> It is infinitely more credible that we, miserable beings, wanderers from the bright path of knowledge [he continued], should be incapable of comprehending the method of the Supreme Artificer in his wondrous and wise machinery, than that a coarse smith should be but a rude admirer of the exquisitely elegant workmanship of a watch. The brain is the source of sense and motion. It is the storehouse of thought and memory as well. Yet no diligent contemplation of its structure will tell us how so coarse a substance (a mere pulp, and that not over-nicely wrought), should subserve so noble an end. No one, either, can determine, from the nature and structure of its parts, whether this or that faculty would be exerted.[2]

Boyle, Hooke, Wren, and Sydenham's other friends went further. They believed that animal experiments, post-mortem examinations, chemical analyses of the body fluids, studies in gross and microscopic anatomy would all eventually throw some light on the causation of disease. Sydenham, on the other hand, thought that medicine would only be truly advanced along the threefold paths of diligently studying the natural histories of diseases; improving therapy by carefully observing patients' responses; and continuing the search for further specific remedies.

Boyle and Sydenham did, however, share a common theory concerning the causation of epidemic fevers. This was not, of course, Sydenham's primary interest. But he did, on one occasion, give his views on the cause of epidemics wherein he incorporated many of Boyle's ideas. The concept of the spread of disease by contagion had long been known, but during the seventeenth century the miasmatic doctrine of epidemics came to the fore. It was thought that an infective principle was diffused in the air in some mysterious way. When these aerial emanations were adversely influenced by the weather, epidemics broke out. The droughts which preceded the pestilential fevers of 1624/5 and 1665[3] added substance to the belief that extreme variations in the weather were, in some way, the precipitating factor. As a chemist and corpuscularian, Boyle was more specific. He postulated that

[1] Sydenham's attitude to the basic medical sciences has been fully analysed by David E. Wolfe, *Bull. Hist. Med.* (1961), **35**, 193–220.
[2] Thomas Sydenham, *op. cit.*, vol. II, p. 84.
[3] Charles Creighton, *A History of Epidemics in Britain* (1892), vol. II, p. 33.

epidemics were caused by subterranean effluvia rendered noxious in the air by association with other corpuscles, and he assumed that these miasmata emanated from deposits in the earth's crust. His theory was really a slight modification of Greek atomism, according to which all matter was thought to consist of minute particles or atoms linked with hooks and eyes into larger combinations called "moleculae". Boyle called them corpuscles instead. Assuming this atomic theory of aerial emanation to be true, then a thorough study of both the weather and the mortality rates would be fruitful fields of inquiry: it was these aspects of the problem that interested several of Sydenham's friends.

> The physicians of our society [wrote Wren], should be desired to give us a good account of all epidemical diseases of the year; histories of any new disease that shall happen; changes in the old; difference of operations in medicine according to the weather and seasons, both inwardly and in wounds; to this should be added a due consideration of the weekly and annual Bills of Mortality in London.[1]

Hooke drew up details of a *Method of Making a History of the Weather* n order to find "what affects are produc'd upon other bodys, as aches in the bodys of man, as what diseases are most rife as colds, feavers, agues, etc. or what other changes are produced".[2] Several others were busy investigating various aspects of the weather in relation to epidemics: Hooke and Wren invented and perfected several meteorological instruments; Locke kept a daily weather register for nearly forty years; and Petty made a study of the London mortality bills.

Although Sydenham did not directly concern himself with research into the variations in the weather and its effect on the mortality rates, he did follow the work of his friends. And his writings on the cause of epidemics reveal that he accepted Boyle's theory without either naming his source, or committing himself too deeply.

> Whether the inward bowels of the earth undergo various changes by the vapours which exhale there from, so that the air is tainted or whether the atmosphere be changed by some alteration induced by some peculiar conjunction of any of the heavenly bodies, it is a truth, that at particular times the air is stuffed full of particles which are hostile to the economy of the human body, just as at other times it is impregnated with particles which disagree with the bodies of different species of brute animals. At these times, whenever we draw in our breath such noxious and unnatural miasmata, mix them with our blood, and fall into such epidemic diseases as they are apt to engender, Nature calls in fever as her usual instrument for expelling from the blood any hostile

[1] C. Wren, published by S. Wren in *Parentalia* (1750), p. 223.
[2] Quoted in Thomas Sprat, *History of the Royal Society* (1959), ed. Jackson I. Cope and Harold Whitmore Jones, Appendix C, p. 75.

matters that may lurk in it. Such diseases are usually called *epidemic*. They are acute and brief, their movement being quick and violent. But besides these diseases excited by some external cause, there are others equally acute, arising from some anomaly or dyscrasis of particular bodies, rather than from any general atmospheric influence. These I call *intercurrent* or *sporadic* inasmuch as they occur during any year whatever.[1]

This corpuscular theory was as good as any other explanation of epidemics in a pre-bacteriological age; and the fact that Sydenham accepted it, shows that in spite of his protests, he occasionally strayed from his chosen sphere of clinical medicine in order to share his friend's hypotheses. But although it can be demonstrated that he based some of his medical nosology on the theories of Bacon, Boyle, and Hippocrates, Sydenham often modified their hypotheses and, unlike many of his contemporaries, abruptly cast them aside whenever empirical facts exposed their fallacies.

[1] Thomas Sydenham, *op. cit.*, vol. II, p. 138.

PART II

Sydenham's Original Writings

THE evidence that Sydenham originally wrote his major works (*Methodus Curandi Febres* (1666) and *Observationes Medicae* (1676)) in English and had them translated into Latin, is overwhelming. This does not, however, mean that he did not understand Latin, but merely that he was too busy with medical practice to perfect an elegant and scholarly style. Sydenham did, in fact, write some of his later works in Latin. Dr. John Drake translated his *Treatise on Gout and Dropsy*[1] (1683) into English; and the Latin manuscript of his posthumous *Processus Integri*, etc. (1693) was in Sydenham's handwriting when handed to the printer. But the fact that all the drafts of Sydenham's earlier works which have come down to us were written in English suggests that these works were subsequently translated into Latin.

Henry Stubbe first mentioned that Sydenham's *Methodus Curandi Febres* was written in English. " 'Tis true *he* did not pen it in Latine," wrote Stubbe, "but another (Mr. G. H.) for him; and perhaps his skill in *that tongue* may not be such as to know when his thoughts are rightly worded."[2] The translator mentioned was Gilbert Havers of Trinity College, Cambridge. Sydenham's *Observationes Medicae* was translated into Latin by Dr. John Mapletoft to whom the book was gratefully dedicated. It was a good choice as Ward described him as "a very polite Scholar, who wrote Latin elegantly, was a great master of the Greek, and understood well the French, Spanish and Italian languages".[3] Ward confirmed that Havers had translated Sydenham's first book, and Mapletoft most of the others. Three years later, Ward published his evidence.[4] He had been informed by the Reverend John Mapletoft (the doctor's son) that his father had translated all Sydenham's works from the first edition of his *Observationes Medicae* (1676) to his *Treatise on Gout and Dropsy* (1683). The Reverend Mapletoft was certain of the dates from a "particular circumstance, which his father would frequently relate with some pleasantry . . . in order to caution him against inadvertency and other hastiness in doing things".

[1] Sydenham's hand trembled to such an extent that he called on Dr. John Drake to help him to write this treatise (Thomas Sydenham, *op. cit.*, vol. II, p. 122). The manuscript of Drake's translation into English is in the Library of the Royal College of Physicians of London.

[2] Henry Stubbe, *An Epistolary Discourse Concerning Phlebotomy* (1671), p. 180.

[3] John Ward, *Lives of the Professors of Gresham College* (1740), p. 277.

[4] John Ward, *The Gentleman's Magazine* (1743), **13**, 528–30.

The doctor, it seems, after he had translated that discourse, sent his manuscript to Dr. Sydenham [Ward continued], who, in return, rallied him in a jocose and friendly manner, for having used the word hydrops always in the feminine gender. It not a little surprised him, how he could possibly have run into such a repeated mistake merely from inattention; and furnished him with a useful lesson for his son to avoid the like. This was about the time that Dr. Mapletoft took orders. And as he then bid farewell to physick, it is not to be wondered at, that the *Schedula Monitoria*, which Dr. Sydenham did not write till the year 1686, was translated by another hand. And that Mr. Havers was the person, who did it, I have lately been assured by two eminent gentlemen of the profession.

Latham[1] examined Mapletoft's Gresham College lectures, published in Latin, which he described as being "over idiomatic", and he regarded Sydenham's Latin as having similar characteristics. Furthermore, the unacademic nature of Sydenham's early life, and the statements of several contemporaries all indicate that he was inadequately grounded in formal learning.

"Oh! what a misery is much study, and how many scruples is this Dr. Sydenham freed from by suffering our best Writers to remain untouched, unstudied," wrote Henry Stubbe.[2] His "chamber-fellow" at All Souls, Dr. Thomas Millington, mentioned to Lord Pembroke (from whom the report found its way into Stukeley's family memoirs) that Sydenham had entirely forgotten his Latin on his return from the Civil War, but recovered it by reading Cicero.[3] And his former pupil, Sir Richard Blackmore, regarded Sydenham as one who reached the highest rank of physicians "without Great Erudition and the Knowledge of Books".[4] Finally, Comrie[5] summarized Sydenham's original writings in this passage:

Sydenham had some doubts as to the perfection of his Latin composition, and his works are obviously translations, as one may judge from the studiously idiomatic nature of many phrases employed; and it is highly probable that the resetting was either effected or revised by some of the author's friends, whose Latinity was more perfect than his own.

Sydenham himself provides the most important evidence as all his extant manuscripts are in English. They are to be found in various libraries. One copy of his *Theologia Rationalis* is in Cambridge University Library, and two more complete ones are in the British Museum.

[1] Thomas Sydenham, *op. cit.*, vol. 1, p. lxii.
[2] Henry Stubbe, *op. cit.*, p. 222.
[3] *The Family Memoirs of the Rev. William Stukeley, M.D.* (1882), Surtees Society, 73, vol. 1, p. 70.
[4] Richard Blackmore, *A Treatise on Smallpox* (1723), p. xi.
[5] Thomas Sydenham (1922), *Selected Works*, ed. J. D. Comrie, pp. 13–14.

This treatise on natural theology provides a rational argument for the existence of God and the immortality of the soul from which Sydenham deduced reasons for leading a virtuous life. It is perfectly consistent with our knowledge of his devout Puritanism.

In the Library of the Royal College of Physicians of London is Sydenham's *Tractatus de Podagra et Hydrope* (1683) passed on to the College by Dr. James Drake who helped him to write it. Another College manuscript presented by Mr. P. Vaillant, who married one of Sydenham's granddaughters, is entitled *Medical Observations* (1669). It is virtually the third unpublished edition of his *Methodus Curandi Febres* (1666) later expanded into his *Observationes Medicae* (1676). Nearly all this manuscript was published by Latham.[1]

The Public Record Office has two uncompleted fragments, *De Arte Medica*[2] (1669) and *Anatomie*[3] (1668), intended to form chapters of a book wherein Sydenham proposed to show that experience was much more important in medical practice than the current stress on the basic sciences. "Dr. Sydenham is writing a book which will bring physitians about his ears," wrote John Ward,[4] "to decrie the usefulness of natural philosophie, and to maintaine the necessitie of knowledg in anatomie *in subordination* to physic." Ward clearly referred to Sydenham's uncompleted book *De Arte Medica* of which *Anatomie* was meant to form part. Both these essays are in the handwriting of John Locke, apart from one sentence in *Anatomie* written by Sydenham. Hence, Fox Bourne[5] and Gibson[6] assumed that they were, in fact, Locke's work. When these essays were written, Locke was Sydenham's occasional amanuensis, and several other fragments in Locke's handwriting are now known to be copies of Sydenham's writings, or his rough drafts hastily dictated to Locke. They clearly reflect Sydenham's more mature clinical experience, and they were written when Locke (who then had a strong iatrochemical bias) was only just beginning his clinical apprenticeship. Furthermore, Sydenham expressed opinions similar to those in *De Arte Medica* and *Anatomie* in his *Observationes Medicae*.[7]

Sydenham endeavoured to trace the relative importance of clinical

[1] Thomas Sydenham, *Works* (1848), ed. R. G. Latham, vol. I, pp. li–lvi; and vol. II, Note A, pp. 379–82; Note B, pp. 383 and 387.

[2] P.R.O., 30/24/47/2, ff. 38–47.

[3] *Ibid.*, ff. 60–7.

[4] *Diary of the Reverend John Ward, M.A. (1648–1679)* (1839), ed. Charles Severn, pp. 241–2.

[5] H. R. Fox Bourne in his *The Life of John Locke* (1876), vol. I, pp. 222–7 presented a modernized version of *De Arte Medica.*

[6] There are several omissions from A. G. Gibson's edition of *De Arte Medica* in his *The Physician's Art* (1933), pp. 13–26.

[7] Thomas Sydenham, *Works*, vol. I, pp. 11–12 and 22–3; and vol. II, pp. 170–2.

experience: method "founded upon philosophy and hypothesis"; botany, chemistry, and anatomy: he intended to set forth the contributions of each of these subjects to medical progress, and show in what way each of them had fallen short of this objective. After acknowledging that anatomical knowledge was of value to surgeons, and a help to the physician in the right application of topical remedies, Sydenham continued: "But that anatomie is like to afford any great improvement to the practise of physic, or assist a man in the findeing out and establishing a true method, I have reason to doubt." He then went on to dismiss microscopic anatomy as useless although he had been prepared to help Robert Hooke's researches in this field. When Hooke wished to examine the small cavities in sage leaves in order to determine whether a small spider lurked in them, he asked Sydenham for a specimen. "I have not been able to meet with Dr. Sydenham," wrote Hooke[1] to Boyle, "all this morning and so cannot send any of the sage, for their was none left in my Lady's[2] house." Sydenham may well have had some support from Boyle who thought that research into the subtle juices of the body rather than its structure would be a more fruitful field of inquiry.

> I will not be so rash as to say, that to mind (as too many Anatomists have done) [he wrote in the Preface of his *Memoirs of the Natural History of Humane Blood*],[3] the Solid parts of the Body, and overlook Enquiries into the Fluids, and especially the Blood, were little less improper in a Physician, than it would be in a Vintner to be very solicitous about the Structure of his Cask, and neglect the consideration of the Wine contained in it.

Another essay, *Tussis*,[4] also in the Public Record Office, was written by Locke with the exception of one sentence in Sydenham's handwriting. Yet this essay is known to be a copy of Sydenham's work. When Locke copied it into his notebook[5] he signified at the end that these were Sydenham's observations.

More copies of Sydenham's original writings are to be found in a manuscript notebook[6] at the Bodleian Library which was once in the possession of Dr. Charles Goodall.[7] After Sydenham's death, Goodall intended to publish a memoir on him, and in 1703 he solicited Sir Hans Sloane for material.

[1] Boyle, *op. cit.*, vol. VI, p. 483.
[2] Boyle's sister, Lady Ranelagh, Sydenham's neighbour in Pall Mall.
[3] Robert Boyle, *Memoirs of the Natural History of Humane Blood* (1683/4), Preface, p. ii.
[4] P.R.O., 30/24/47/2, ff. 31–4 verso.
[5] B.L., MS. Locke, c. 42, f. 258.
[6] B.L., MS. Rawlinson, c. 406.
[7] Discussed in Kenneth Dewhurst's "Some Letters of Dr. Charles Goodall (1642–1712) to Locke, Sloane, and Sir Thomas Millington", *J. Hist. Med.* (1962), **17**, 487–508.

Good doctor, I fully purpose to publish some posthumous Works of my father and your good friend, Dr. Sydenham. Upon this account [continued Goodall],[1] I waited upon his son to request him to supply me with what memoirs his father left. He told me that what he had were put into your hands, and that if you pleased he should be very willing they should be printed by me. This is therefore to request you to let me know whether you are willing to part with them that I may do right to the Author now dead, as I honoured him whilst living.

Goodall arranged for an amanuensis to copy Sydenham's manuscripts in Sloane's possession, and these papers have found their way to the Bodleian Library. Sydenham's accounts of various diseases, written in English, are specifically stated to have been copied from his original manuscripts, whereas the Latin extracts are merely Sydenham's verbal opinions put into Latin by the writer as was the usual practice. The Latin passages are marginally marked "ex ore Syd.". The whole of these manuscripts were published by Dr. W. A. Greenhill in his *Anecdota Sydenhamiana* (1845), and also by Latham.[2]

Also in the Bodleian Library amongst the Lovelace Collection of Locke's manuscripts are several medical notes, all written in English, which represent parts of an early draft of Sydenham's *Observationes Medicae* (1676). One heavily corrected manuscript entitled *Of the Four Constitutions*[3] is all in Sydenham's hand; other notes on "a dysentery",[4] "febres intercurrentes",[5] "pleurisie",[6] and "febres intermittentes"[7] are in Locke's handwriting though they clearly represent Sydenham's opinions. Herein, Sydenham frequently referred to his earlier writings on these diseases, and proof of their authorship is to be found in another of Locke's medical notebooks[8] wherein he copied these essays in shorthand and stated at the end of each one that Sydenham had written it. This notebook also contains a long, neatly written treatise on smallpox in Locke's handwriting.[9] Only the opening sentence is in Latin, which may be translated as follows: "The Treatise on Smallpox, dated 1669, of the author's very good friend and master, Dr. Thomas Sydenham, a man of great learning, and a most successful practitioner."[10]

[1] B.M., MS. Sloane, 4039, f. 253.
[2] Thomas Sydenham, *Works*, vol. II, Appendix C, pp. 325–78.
[3] MS. Locke, c. 19, ff. 170–6.
[4] *Ibid.*, c. 29, ff. 19–20.
[5] *Ibid.*, f. 21.
[6] *Ibid.*, ff. 23–4.
[7] *Ibid.*, ff. 25–8.
[8] B.L., MS. Locke, c. 21, ff. 40, 61, 66, 82. On the first page of this notebook is a prescription in Sydenham's handwriting.
[9] *Ibid.*, ff. 3–17.
[10] "Sagacissimi viri et practici faelicissi[mi] Dni Dris Thomae Sydenham amici sui plurimum Colendi tractatus de Variolis an. 1669."

Again at the end of the essay Locke added this concise statement as to the author: "Written by that Great Genius of Physick Dr. Sydenham in July 1669." A preface and dedication, in Locke's hand, to the first Earl of Shaftesbury, are in the Public Record Office.[1] Internal evidence shows that these heavily corrected manuscripts were hurriedly written by Locke on Sydenham's behalf, and probably at his dictation. Sydenham originally intended to publish the whole essay separately. But he published nothing after the second edition of his *Methodus Curandi Febres* (1668) until his *Observationes Medicae* (1676) came out eight years later. Why was this treatise laid aside? Both medical and political reasons probably caused him to abandon it. Sydenham was constantly modifying his opinions in the light of further experience, and he decided to recast and expand the whole of his earlier book as *Observationes Medicae*, into which he eventually incorporated this treatise on smallpox in a chapter headed: "Regular Smallpox during the years 1667, 1668 and part of 1669."[2] But in order to explain his subsequent omission of the preface and dedication it is necessary to trace the movements of Locke, Mapletoft, and Lord Shaftesbury between 1669 and 1676.

Mapletoft, who eventually translated Sydenham's book into Latin, was in Copenhagen with the diplomatic mission of the Earl of Essex in 1669, and Locke had replaced him as Sydenham's closest colleague. He was still abroad on 10 July, 1670 when Locke added this postscript to his letter:[3] "Dr. Sydenham desires to be very kindly remembered to you." Two years later Mapletoft accompanied the Countess of Northumberland during her travels in France. Locke had now become more heavily engaged in affairs of State, following Shaftesbury's promotion to Lord Chancellor in 1672, and he bemoaned the fact that his duties allowed him little time for medicine. "Dr. Sydenham and I mention you sometimes,"[4] he informed Mapletoft, "for we do not now meet often, my business now allowing me but little leisure for visits, but I hope I shall in a short space bring it to better terms." He did. After taking a medical degree at Oxford, Locke left for France at the beginning of 1675 and remained there for the next three and a half years. Hence, at various times Sydenham lacked both Locke's secretarial aid and Mapletoft's services as a potential translator. Locke was in Montpellier when Mapletoft informed him that Sydenham's *Observationes Medicae* (1676) had appeared; in the same letter he learned that Shaftesbury was a prisoner in the Tower. Times had changed. Had

[1] P.R.O., 30/24/47/2, ff. 50–2 and ff. 54–61.
[2] Thomas Sydenham, *op. cit.*, vol. 1, pp. 121–51.
[3] *European Magazine* (1785), **14**, 321.
[4] *Ibid.* (1788), **14**, 402, 14 February, 1672/3.

Sydenham wished to use the original dedication (which was most unlikely) he would have been unable to get the manuscript which was with Locke's other papers at Exeter House, while the distinguished patron to whom it was to be dedicated was locked up in the Tower.

These fragments of Sydenham's writings show some characteristic features. They are written in a straightforward, robust, seventeenth-century style with plain medical facts interspersed with the occasional picturesque phrase. They were all hastily written, and Sydenham tended to be repetitive: the fact that numerous after-thoughts were inserted in the margins suggests that they were dictated, probably on account of Sydenham's physical disabilities. Some of Sydenham's more forceful attacks on his critics have been toned down in translation, and a strong dash of classical erudition added instead. Here is an example of Sydenham's original English:

> But now in the flox pox the day of the greatest danger and wherein most die is eleventh from the invasion for the matter of the ptyalisme which till now was crude thin and easy to bring up is at this time become viscouse and baked up....

Latham's translation from the Latin version reads:

> In confluent smallpox the patients run the most risk, and most generally die on the eleventh day. This is the day whereon the salivation, which has hitherto been a safeguard to the patient generally ceases of itself.[1]

This is another original passage from Sydenham's essay on smallpox (1669):

> This veryly notwithstanding the great and unreasonable prejudice entertained by the world against the same, is the true and genuin way of keepeing those that are sick of this disease, and will be found to be soe when I am in my grave.

The translation by Latham reads:

> This is the true and genuine method of treating this sort of smallpox, and however much it may be opposed by the great and unfounded prejudice of the partisans of an opposite practice, it is the method which will prevail when I am dead.[2]

It is now necessary to offer a brief explanation of the methods I have adopted in transcribing these manuscripts. Such obvious abbreviations as yt (that), ye (the), wch (which), sd (said), agn (again), pts (parts),

[1] Thomas Sydenham, *Works*, vol. I, p. 130, para. 21.
[2] *Ibid.*, p. 142, para. 48.

wt (what), magnt. (management), mencōnd (mentioned), observacōns (observations), have been expanded in the text. Less obvious abbreviations such as phia (philosophia), nāal (natural), māal (material), 3^{an} (tertian), 4^{an} (quartan), rig (rigor), hor (horror) have also been expanded. The symbols § (venesection or bleeding) and MM (methodus medendi) have been simply rendered as bleeding and method of treatment. Sydenham's abbreviated Latin prescriptions remain unaltered, and an English translation has been added as a footnote. Apothecaries' symbols for scruple, drachm, and ounce have been replaced by the modern equivalents. The abbreviations B.L. (Bodleian Library), B.M. (British Museum), and P.R.O. (Public Record Office) have been used to indicate the sources of some of the documents quoted.

Several manuscripts contain numerous footnotes and marginal notes which have been reproduced here in the main text in order to maintain continuity. Sometimes Sydenham indicated the appropriate places in the text for the insertion of these marginal notes which are here rendered within pointed brackets. Other marginal notes, enclosed here within square brackets, have been incorporated into the main text in accordance with the meaning of the whole passage, but *without* any appropriate indication from Sydenham. In all other respects the text is unaltered, apart from the insertion of a minimum of punctuation wherever its absence leads to obscurity.

DE ARTE MEDICA OR ARS MEDICA, 1669[1]

Length of life with freedome from infirmity and pain as much as the constitution of our fraile composure is capable of is of soe great concernment to man kinde, that there can scarce be found any greater undertakeing then the profession to cure diseases, nor is there any art that soe well deserves all the care and industry and observation of its professors to improve it and bring it to perfection, which I doubt not but in many parts and to a great degree it is capable of. He that shall goe about to doe this shall noe question deserve the thanks of mankinde for soe good an intention, as the reduceing those rules and methods to a certainty, on the practise whereof the ease and recovery of sicke men depends, but whoever shall thinke to compass it alone will finde him selfe ingaged in a business too large for any one mans comprehension and too great for his owne single endeavours. My intention therefor is to propose some few things to the consideration of the Learned men of this soe usefull a faculty, and to excite their mutuall assistance to perfect the art and establish a setled certaine practise in the cure of sicknesses, that soe the large catalogue of yet incurable diseases and the frequent sad events of the rest being every day lessened [the diffidence which some sober men upon serious consideration seeme to have of the art its self and the disrepute which others industriously labour to bring upon the practise of physick being by the dayly growing successe of the physicians removed, industrious and learned practitioners][2] of physick [may] with more confidence and satisfaction attend their calling when they could be noe longer upbraided with those confessed opprobria medicorum which every day yeild to the efficacy of their medecins or well orderd methods. If this were once set about, it would not perhaps be found soe impossible a designe as is at first sight imagind, and the great improvement some parts of medecin have received within this few years give me confidence to believe that it is yet capable of great additions and that in a way some thing

[1] P.R.O., 30/24/47/2, ff. 38–47. Two editions of this essay have been published. H. R. Fox Bourne in his *The Life of John Locke* (1876), vol. I, pp. 222–7 presented a version in modern spelling. A. G. Gibson's *The Physician's Art* (1933), pp. 13–26 is incomplete as he omitted the quotation from Cicero together with several sentences written on the opposite page of the manuscript and included in square brackets in this text. Both Fox Bourne and Gibson stated that Locke was the author. Two passages in Sydenham's writings express views similar to those in this essay (*Works*, vol. II, pp. 11–12 and 22–3).

[2] An insertion—not properly worked into the text—"may" is an editorial addition.

different from what hitherto seems to have beene generally followed by most of those who have beene soe kinde as to propagate the knowledge of physick and leave the rules of practise to posteryty,[1] as will appear to any one who shall carefully peruse their wrightings, wherein yet they have very much obleiged posteryty, and they are not to be blamed that they did that which is very agreeable to the nature of mans understanding, which not contenting its self to observe the operation of nature and the event of things, is very inquisitive after their cause, and very restlesse and unquiet till, in those things which it is conversant about, it has framed to its self some hypothesis and laid a foundation whereon to establish all its reasonings. If therefor the Learned men of former ages imploid a great part of their time and thoughts in searching out the hidden causes of distempers, were curious in imagining the secret workmanship of nature and the severall unperceptible tools wherwith she wrought, and puting all these phansies togeather fashioned to themselves systems and hypotheses, is noe more to be wondered at or censured, then that they accommodated them selves to the fashion of their times and countrys, and soe far complied with their most naturall inclinations, as to desire to have some basis to rest their thoughts upon and some grounds to guide them in the practise of their art, their being busy and subtile in disputing upon alloud principles was but to be imploid in the way of fame and reputation and the learning valued in that age, and that their practise extended noe farther then the sacred principles they beleived in would permit is noe more to be admired then that we finde noe fair and lasting fabriques left to us by our ancestors upon narrow and unsound foundations. I would not be thought here to censure the learned authors of former times, or disowne the advantages they have left to posterity. To them we owe a great number of excellent observations and severall ingenious discourses, and there is not any one rule of practise founded upon unbiassed observation which I do not receive and submitt to with veneration and acknowledgment: yet I think I may confidently affirme, that those hypothesis which tied the long and elaborate discourses of the ancientts, and suffered not their enquirys to extend them selves any farther then how the phenomena of diseases might be explaind by these doctrines and the rules of practise accommodated

[1] On the page facing there is this Latin quotation:
"Verum ego hanc vim esse intelligo in praeceptis omnibus, non ut ea secuti oratores eloquentiae laudem sint adepti, sed quae sua sponte homines eloquentes facerent ea quosdam observasse atque in artem redigisse; non eloquentiam ex artificio sed artificium ex eloquentia natum. Cic. de oratore. l. i. c. 6."
["But to my thinking the virtue in all rules is, not that orators by following them have won a reputation for eloquence, but that certain persons have noted and reduced to an art the doings of men who were naturally eloquent; eloquence is not the offspring of the art, but the art of eloquence."]

to the receivd principles, has at last but confined and narrowed mens thoughts, amused their understanding with fine but uselesse speculations, and diverted their enquirys from the true and advantageous knowledg of things. The notions that have been raised into mens heads by remote speculative principles though true are like the curious imagery men sometimes see in the clouds which they are pleased to call the heavens, which though they are for the most part phantasticall and at best but the accidentall contexture of a mist yet doe really hinder the sight and shorten the prospect. And though these painted aparitions are raisd by the sun and seeme the genuin ofspring of the great fountain of light, yet they are really noething but darknesse and a cloud, and whosoever shall travell with his eye fixed on these 'tis ten to one goes out of his way. He that in Physick shall lay downe fundamentall maximes and from thence drawing consequence and raising dispute shall reduce it into the regular forme of a science has indeed done something to enlarge the art of talkeing and perhaps laid a foundation for endless disputes. But if he hopes to bring men by such a system to the knowledg of the infirmities of mens bodys, the constitution nature signes changes and history of diseases with the safe and direct way of their cure, [he] takes much what a like course with him that should walke up and downe in a thick wood overgrowne with briers and thornes with a designe to take a view and draw a map of the country. These speculative theorems doe as little advantage the physick as food of men. And he that thinks he came to be skild in diseases by studying the doctrine of the humors, that the notions of obstructions and putrefaction assists him in the cure of feavers, or that by the acquaintance he has with sulphur and mercury he was lead into this useful discovery, that what medecines and regimen as certainely kill in the latter end of some feavers as they cure in others, may as rationaly beleive that his Cooke owes his skill in rosting and boyling to his study of the elements and that his speculations about fire and water have taught him that the same seething liquors that boiles the egg hard makes the hen tender. The begining and improvement of useful arts, and the assistances of human life, have all sprung from industry and observation; true knowledg grew first in the world by experience and rationall operations; and had this method beene continued and all mens thoughts beene imploid to adde their own tryalls to the observation of others noe question physick, as well as many other arts, had been in a far better condition then now it is. But proud man, not content with that knowledg he was capable of and was useful to him, would needs penetrate into the hidden causes of things, lay downe principles and establish maximes to him self about the operations of nature, and then vainely expect that Nature, or in truth God him self, should proceede according to those laws his maximes had prescribed him. Whereas his narrow weake facultys could reach noe farther then the observation and memory of some few effects produced by visible and externall causes but in a way utterly out of the reach of his apprehension, it being perhaps noe absurdity to thinke that this great and curious fabrique of the world the workmanship of the almighty cannot be perfectly comprehended by any understanding but his that made it, man still affecting something of a deity laboured to make his imagination supply what his observation failed him in, and when he could not discover the principles and causes and methods of natures workmanship, he would needs fashion all those out of his owne thought, and make a world to him self, framed and governed by his owne intelligence, [and thus man by desire to know more than was fit a second time lost the little remainder of knowledg that was left him.][1] This vanity spread its self into many of the useful parts of naturall philosophy, and by how much the more it seemed subtile sublime or learned by soe much the more it proved pernicious and hurtful by hindering the growth of practicall knowledg. Thus the most acute and ingenious part of men being by custom and education ingaged in empty speculations, the improvement of usefull arts was lefte to the meaner sort of people who had weaker parts and lesse opportunitys to doe it, and were therfor branded with the disgracefull name of mechaniques. Hence it came to passe that the world was fild with books and disputes, and that books multiplied without the increase of knowledg: the ages successively grew more learned without being wiser or happyer, or if the conveniencys of humane life chanced to be promoted by any new invention, men were not led to such happy discoverys by the conduct of philosophicall speculations, but chance or well-designed experiments taught them to those who imploid their time and thoughts about the works of nature more then the maxims of the schooles. Of this the plowman tanners smiths bakers dier painter etc are witnesses. The great inventions of powder and the loadstone, which have altered the whole affairs of man kinde are undeniable instances. Soe that those who had read and writt whole volumes of generation and corruption knew not the way to preserve or propagate the meanest species of creatures, he that could dispute learnedly of nutrition concoction and assimulation, was beholding yet to the cooke and the good housewife, for a wholesome and savoury meale, and whoever desired to have faire gardens and fruitfull fields, had more reason to consult the experience of the dull plowman and unread gardener then the profound philosopher or acute

[1] Insertion from facing page.

disputant. Let not any one be offended that I ranke the cooke and the Farmer with the Schollar and Philosopher, For speakeing here of the knowledg of naturall bodys, the end and benefit whereof can be noe other then the advantages and conveniencys of human life, all speculations in this subject however curious or refined or seemeing profound and solid, if they teach not their followers to doe something either better or in a shorter and easier way then otherwise they could, or else leade them to the discovery of some new and usefull invention, deserve not the name of knowledg, or soe much as the wast time of our idle howers to be throwne away upon such empty idle phylosophy. They that are studiously busy in the cultivateing and adorning such drie barren notions are vigorously imploid to little purpose, and might with as much reason have retained now they are men the babys they made when they were children, as exchanged them for those empty impracticall notions that are but the puppets of mens phansys and imaginations which, however dressed up, after 40 years dandleing are but puppets still, void of strength use or activity. But not to expatiat into the large field of naturall phylosophy where perhaps the foundation of the mischeif was first laid, I shall according to my designe confine my self at present to that branch of it which immeadiatly concerns the health of men, and in physick shall consider—

(1) The present state of the faculty of Medecine as it now stands in reference to Diseases and their cure.

(2) The severall degrees and steps whereby it grew to that heigth it is at present arrived to, which I suppose are these following—(1) Experience. (2) Method founded upon Phylosophy and Hypothesis. (3) Botaniques. (4) Chymistry. (5) Anatomy. In all which I shall indeavour to shew how much each hath contributed to the advanceing the Art of Physick, and wherein they came short of perfecting it.

(3) What yet may be further donne towards the more speedy and certain cure of diseases; i.e. By what means and method the practise of physick may be brought nearer to perfection.

I. Diseases as they lye under the regimen of physick, and receive more or lesse check from the applications and methods of that art as it now stands, may fitly be divided into 4 sorts. 1. Such as are almost perfectly under the controule of medecin, and doe for the most part constantly yeild to the skillfull physitians hand guided by the established rules of his art, and wherein he can at first sight, (as far as is fit with submission to providence and the great disposer of mens lives) undertake the cure with assurance of a happy event. For it is not to be hoped that the meanest disease should always obey the skill of the ablest physitian nor would such a vanity be tolerable in weake ignorant men to pretend to be the dispensers of health and life that are the free gifts of almighty god,[1] and which though his hand uncontroulably takes away or bestows where he pleases, yet he most commonly does it by the intervention of fit secondary means; and therefor I doubt not but a physitian in some cases may with as little presumption assure a sick man of recovery, as a mother undertakes to cure the hunger of her childe, which is a disease too, but yet this he doth not by any power or authority of his owne over the nature of things, but by a right application of those remedys which were ordeined for the produceing such effects, medeceins rightly ordered being as certaine to recover some infirme bodys as rabits and chicken well dressed to nourish others that are healthy, though perhaps some constitutions may be found with whome that kinde even of wholesome diet will not at all agree. But yet, whoever has brought the cure of any disease neare such a certainty as is the nourishment of a healthy man by any one kinde of holesome meat, may be allowed to be confident in his undertaking that species of distemper and in that part to have perfected the art of physick, though perhaps in some stubborne and irregular cases his well constituted method should faile him, and the disease frustrate the usuall successe of his indeavours. And to such a degree of perfection as this I thinke I may confidently affirme the art of physick is arrived in many diseases which seldom stand out against the skillfull attempts of good practitioners. Nor let the malice of prejudiced persons suggest here, that these confident promises of health are not to be relied [on] but only in such diseases which of them selves leave us, wherein nature commonly workes the cure without the assistance of art and it may be with reason suspected the patient owed his recovery more to the vigor of his owne constitution then the apothecarys drugs, some diseases like some weeds. . . .

[1] On facing page is this reference: "Novum Organ. l. i, S. 31, 32."

ANATOMIE, 1668[1]

[The opening sentence is in Sydenham's handwriting.]

Others of them have more pompously and speciously prosecuted the promoting of this art by searching into the bowels of dead and living creatures, as well sound as diseased, to find out the seeds of discharging them, but with how little success such endeavours have bin or are like to be attended I shall here in some measure make appear.

[The rest of the essay is in Locke's handwriting.]

Anatomie noe question is absolutely necessary to a Chirurgen and to a physitian who would direct a surgeon in incision trepanning and several other operations. It often too directs the physician's hand in the right application of topicall remedys and his judgment in the prognostique of wounds, humors and severall other organicall diseases. It may too in many cases satisfie a physician in the effects he finds produced by his method or medicines, and though it gives him not a full account of the causes or their ways of operation, yet may give him some light in the observation of diseases and the ideas he shall frame of them, which, though not perhaps true in it self, yet will be a great help to his memory and guide to his practise. And not least it will be always thought an advantage for a physician to know as much of the subject he has to deal with as is possible. But that anatomie is like to afford any great improvement to the practise of physic, or assist a man in the findeing out and establishing a true method, I have reason to doubt. All that Anatomie can doe is only to shew us the gross and sensible parts of the body, or the vapid and dead juices all which, after the most diligent search, will be noe more able to direct a physician how to cure a disease than how to make a man; for to remedy the defects of a part whose organicall constitution and that texture whereby it operates, he cannot possibly know, is alike hard, as to make a part which he knows not how is made. Now it is certaine and beyond controversy that nature performs all her operations on the body by parts so minute and insensible that I thinke noe body will ever hope or pretend, even by the assistance of glasses or any other invention, to come to a sight of them, and to tell us what organicall texture or what kinde of ferment (for whether it be done by one or both of these ways is yet a question and

[1] P.R.O., 30/24/47/2, ff. 60–7. Sydenham used similar, though less strongly worded arguments in his writings (*Works*, vol. II, pp. 170–2).

like to be soe always notwithstanding all the endeavours of the most accurate dissections) separate any part of the juices in any of the viscera, or tell us of what liquors the particles of these juices are, or if this could be donne (which yet is never like to be) would it at all contribute to the cure of the diseases of those very parts which we so perfectly knew. For suppose any one shall have so sharp a knife and sight as to discover the secret and effective composure of any part could he make an occular demonstration that the pores of the parenchyma of the liver or kidneys were either round or square and that the parts of urin and gall separated in these parts were in size and figure answerable to those pores. I ask how this would at all direct him in the cure either of the jaundice or stoppage of urin? What would this advantage his method or guide him to fit medicins? How knows he hereby that rhubarb or pellitory have in them fit wedges to divide the blood into such parts as may be separable, urin in the one, or gall in the other, or any other particles in them fitted to open these passages. How regulate his dose, to mix his simples and to prescribe all in a due method? All this is only from history and the advantage of a diligent observation of these diseases, of their beginning, progress, and ways of cure, which a physician may as well doe without a scrupulous enquiry into the anatomye of the parts, as a gardener may by his art and observation, be able to ripen, meliorate and preserve his fruit without examining what kindes of juices, fibres, pores etc. are to be found in the roots, barke, or body of the tree. An undeniable instance of this we have in the illiterate Indians, who by enquirys suitable to wise though unlearned men, had found out the ways of cureing many diseases which exceeded the skill of the best read doctors that came out of Europe, who were better versed in Anatomy than those skillful Indians, who were so far from makeing any dissections that they had not soe much as knives. And yet the Christians chose to trust them selves in their hands and found help from them when their owne doctors left them as incurable. No question but the dissector may know well the sensible parts of the organs for generation in man or woman by which the pox is conveyed from one to an other. But can he hence discover to me what kinde of venom it is that produces such horrid effects in the body? Why it corrodes this or pains that part of the body? Can his knife discover the receptacles which the nose soe easily affords, more than other parts, or will all his knowledge in the parts of the body point out one fit remedy for it? If therefore anatomie shew us neither the causes nor cures of most diseases I think it is not very likely to bring any great advantages for removeing the pains and maladys of mankind. Tis truth it pretends to teach us the use of the parts, but this, if it doth at all, it doth imperfectly and after a grosse manner. To evince this let us but consider the spleen and enquire what discoverys anatomy hath made in the use of that part, and after all I feare we shall finde that we know little or noe thing of what office it is, and what it contributes to the health or œconomy of the body, all the assigned uses of it being at best but uncertain and useless guesses which may appear in that little alteration hath been observed in those animals whose spleens have beene taken out and they lived long afterwards. Now this proceeds not from any the exceeding curious fabrique and indiscoverable organs and tools of this part above any of the rest that we are soe much at a losse in the functions of this viscus, but only from an inflated opinion of our owne knowledg, and a conceit that we are better acquainted with the operation of other parts than indeed we are. For haveing observed in some of the viscera a separation of some liquor or other, and that by certain vessels for that purpose certain juices are brought out of the part which were noewhere convey'd in by them selves, we presently conclude we know the use of the part, which is true that in gross, and as to some effect we doe, as that gall is separated in the liver, urin in the kidneys, seed in the testicles, etc. But how the parte performes its duty by what engines it divides, precipitates, ferments, separates or what else you please to call it, we know noe more in the liver than in the spleene, nor will anatomy ever instruct us by shewing that gall comes from the liver how it is to be assisted in its defects or corrected in its errors when it does not this aright. Soe that he that does but know the size and situation of the liver, and has seen but some of its large vessels, their entrance in and comeing out of the substance of it, is like to know as much of its operation as he that shall excarnificate it, and spend whole years in traceing the meanders of its vessels. Tis no doubt we see gall and urin comeing from the liver and kidneys, and know these to be the effects of those parts, but are not hereby one jott nearer the cause nor manner of their operation. And he that upon this account shall imagine that he knows the use of the liver better than the spleen in order to his cureing of diseases may upon as good grounds persuade him selfe that he has discovered how nature makes minerall waters in the bowels of the earth better than he does how she makes iron or lead because he sees the one flow out but the other lyes hid within, whereas upon examination it will be found that the workmanship of nature is alike obscure in both. So that I thinke it is cleare that after all our porings and mangling the parts of animals we know noething but the grosse parts, see not the tools and contrivances by which nature works, and are as far off from the discovery we aime at as ever. Soe that he that knows but the natural shape, size, situation and colour of any part is as well learned for the knowing of its diseases, and their cure, as he that can describe all the minute and sensible parts of it, can tell how many veins and arterys it has, and how distributed, count every fibre and describe all the qualitys of the parenchyma. Since he knows all this, and yet not to perceive how it performs its office, is indeed to take pains for something more difficult, but not a jott more usefull, than the other less accurate knowledg in anatomie I mentioned. The laborious anatomist I will not deny knows more, but not more to the purpose, for if he cannot come to discover these little differences which preserve health or make a disease, if he cannot possibly see how nature prepares those juices which serve in their fitt places and proportions for the use and preservation of the body he may perhaps be the better anatomist by multiplying dissections, but not a better physician, for poreing and gazeing on the parts which we dissect without perceiving the very precise way of their working is but still a superficial knowledg, and though we cut into there inside, we see but the outside of things and make but a new superficies for ourselves to stare at. For could the intent looking upon any part teach us to cure its diseases then ladys would have more reason to go to the painter than physician for the removall of freckles and scabs, sore eyes, and sallow cheeks from their faces. But to make it yet clearer that when we pretend to discern by anatomie the use of any parts it is only of these parts where we see something separated, and then all the knowledg we have is but that such a juice is there separated which is but a very scanty and uselesse discovery, and that which in a very few days may be perfectly attained in all the parts of the body. Let us consider the lungs a part of that constant necessity that we cannot live a minute without its exercise. And yet there being noe sensible a separation of anything in this viscus we are still at a perfect loss in its use (not to say anything that though anatomie had taught us its use yet it would not doe us much service towards the cure of its disease) and whether respiration serve to coole the bloud, or give vent to its vapours, or to add a ferment to it, or to pound and mix its minute particles, or whether anything else is in dispute amongst the learned from whose controversys about it are like to arise rather more doubts than any clear determination of the point, and all that anatomie has done in this case as well as severall others is but to offer new conjectures and fresh matter for endless disputations. Tis certain therefore that in parts where no separation is made the anatomist is forced to confesse his ignorance, and but very doubtingly to assign the use of the parte; not that he has any more perfect or usefull knowledge of these parts where he finds a separation. Tis true he affirms it is the business of the liver to separate the Gall and the Pancreas a juice of another kinde, of which we have yet noe name, yet we know as well with all its uses as the gall, and others that we have names for and tis probable he is in the right; but this does him no more service than the bare hearing that it is the businesse of a watchmaker to make a watch will instruct any one the better to make or mend it when out of order. So that I thinke I may, without injury to any body, say that as to the true use of parts and their manner of operation anatomy has hitherto made very slender discoverys. Nor does it give very much hopes of any greater improvement, haveing already baffled the endeavours of soe many learned, ingenious, industrious and able men, not for want of any skill or sagacity in them, but because the matters they handled would not beare it, the tools where with nature works and the changes she produces in these particles being too small and too subtle for the observation of our senses, for when we go about to discover the curious artifice of nature, and take a view of the instruments by which she works, we may by as much reason expect to have a sight of these very spirits by which we hope to see them, for I believe they are as far from the reach of our senses as the other.

Let us next see how anatomie performs its undertaking in detecting the humors and discovering to us their natures and uses, and here I thinke we shall find it performes as little as in the other parts. And that for the same reason for though upon dissection we find severall juices where they are lodged and which way they tend, yet what part they beare in the œconomy of the body, what ferments, strainings, mixtures and other changes they receive in the severall parts through which they pass we cannot at all discover. For wherever allmost the anatomist makes his trialls, either the juices he observes must be dead extravasated and out of the regimen of the life and spirits of the body, or else the animall dead, and soe the parts which alter those juices loose their operation, and which so ever of these two happen, the humour he is examining will be of a far different nature and consideration from what it is when it has its due motion and activity in a living animal. All therefore that the anatomist can doe is to shew us the sensible qualities and motions of severall of the juices of the body, but how little this can possibly conduce to hypothesis or cureing of diseases or preserving the health and easing the maladies of mankinde may well easily appear to a man who considers first that many of these humors can not be known in a living man. For whatever alterations may happen in the chyle, lympha, succus pancreaticus, gall, and what ever other humors be in the body not immediately vented in some outward part, excepting the bloud, and how ever these alterations may concern the present state of health or sicknesse of any man, yet even the sensible qualities of those either natural or depraved juices cannot be known to the physician when he is considering the condition of his patient or the way to his recovery. Secondly that those juices that may come within the observation of the physician as the spittle, seed, urin, bloud etc. are liable to very great alterations in their sensible qualities without discovering any difference of health or sicknesse in the man, and he would be thought a very indiscrete man that upon every change he should find in his urin or spitle he should betake himself to a physician to rectify the disorders of his body: the vanity and quacking of uromantia hath been sufficiently exploded by the learned and sober part of rationall physicians. But, thirdly, grant that these excreta doe give the physician any insight into either the constitution of the body or the condition of the disease, what thanks is there due to Anatomy for it? He that in a feavor or any other malady is able to make advantage from his inspection into the urin, and by that takes any indication, and chooses time for purging, bleeding, or the giving of any medicin, doth not this one jott the better for knowing the structure of the reins, ureters, bladder etc., but by acquainting himself with the nature and history of the disease. And whether the stones be only a complication of vessels without parenchyma, or glandules consisting of vessels and parenchyma, will be of very little consideration when a man finds the excretion and colour of the seed praeternatural in a virulent gonorrhoea, and he that knows all the texture and constitution of that part is as far from knowing the cause of the yellowness or acrimony of the seed at that time, as he that has never seen any more of a testicle than a dish of lambstones fried and served up to a table. The bloud noe question is the great genius of the body, and that which is most concerned in the nourishment, health, and sicknesse of the man (for as for the succus nervosus whatever others may thinke of it 'tis certaine the anatomist of all men, if he be true to his principles, should not suppose it, since he ought not to believe anything but what he sees, and when he makes it visible others may then believe it too) the bloud, I say, that is soe much concerned almost in every disease, is liable to examination without the help of dissection. And he that has but anatomy enough to know a vein and skill enough to use a lancet, or that stands by a surgeon that does, has, if he be a good physician and an observeing man, more information from the bloud and light into the disease than ever he could gain by ripping up all the veins and arteries tracing their branches and meanders in never soe many dead carcases.

But, fourthly, granting all this, that the accurate anatomist knew more of the sensible qualities of the juices of the body and the kinds of their variations than another physician, I think he would after all that know very little more of the causes of diseases than a less accurate dissector. For after all his fine discourses of the taste, smell, colour and consistence of the juices in the body, and the changes he supposes to be the cause of this or that disorder in the body, it is certainly something more subtile and fine than what our senses can take cognisance of that is the cause of the disease, and they are the invisible and insensible spirits that govern preserve and disorder the œconomie of the body. This cannot be doubted by any who will allow themselves to consider how little different the blood as to all its sensible qualities is in severall feavers which are certainly distempers that do affect and reside in the blood, from the blood in a healthy man. Who is able by seeing the blood to divine whether it be an intermittent or a continuall feavor, whether a dysentery or haemoptoe the patient is sick of, and what sensible fault does often appear in that bloud in which nature does sometimes expel the cause of a disease, and give present ease by a critical haemorrhagia wherein the bloud very often looks as florid and as well conditioned as any that flows in the veins of the most healthy man living? Tis something therefore beyond yellow florid or black, something besides acid, sweet, or salin that causes diseases, and appears to us only in the sad effects we feel of it which may be very violent and horrid though the cause be very small in bulk and insensible in its parts. What strange disorder will the bite of a viper cause in the body of the strongest man when all that he injects into the wounded flesh is not the tenth, yea, not the 1/100th part of a grain, and he that shall remember how many thousand men one ounce of vitrum antimon. without wasting itself will vomit infused in wine, wherein it makes no sensible alteration, will have little encouragement to seek for the cause of diseases, in the sensible difference of the humors. Some men that have made anatomical inquiries into the stomach, tell us the menstrum, which there causes appetite and digestion is acid. Others that it is more of kin to sal armoniak, (for the naturall temper of that juice which lies at the threshold and very entrance of the body, and is but the first preparative to those other more refined and exalted that are afterwards to be produced is not yet agreed on after so many thousand dissections) be it acid, or salin, or of what other sensible quality it will, the appetite nor digestion seems not to depend upon the sensible constitution of that menstrum when it often happens that one who sits to table with a good stomach looses it utterly upon the receipt of suddaine bad news, or anything that violently stirs up any passion, and has noe longer any appetite, though nobody can thinke that the juice in the stomach is by such an accident made less acid than it was before. There is something therefore in the body and juices too curious and fine for us to discern which performs the offices in the severall parts, governs the health, and produces the various motions in the body—intus mens agitat molem —and upon whose inconceivable alteration depends our health or sicknesse. Hence a fright which causes such diseases as epilepsies, hysterical fits, and fatuity often cures others as agues, and, as some report, the gout it self; and 'tis probable in these cases 'twould puzzle the quickest sighted anatomist, assisted too by the best microscope, to find any sensible alteration made either in the juices or solid parts of the body.

Therefor this hidden *δημιουργὸς* [1] was soe much out of the reach of the senses, yea and apprehension of the ancients, that not knowing what to conceive it, they went above the clouds for a name and cald it *φύσιν ἀνάλογον τῷ τῶν ἀστρῶν στοιχήῳ*,[2] an expression however obscure and insignificant more like to give us a usefull notion of the thing, than the anatomist to shew us this archeus by which name Helmont has as clearly and intelligibly explained it to us as Aristotle by his description.

But to put it beyond doubt that Anatomie is never like to shew us the minute organs of the parts or subtle particles of the juices on which depend all its operations and our health, it will suffice but to mention a mite or rather a little creature by the help of microscopes lately discovered in some kinde of sand. An animal soe small that it is not to be discerned by the naked eye, and yet has life and motion to the preservation of which there must necessarily be supposed a mouth, stomach, and guts, heart, reins and arteries and juices in them, add to these brains, nerves, muscles, and bones without all which it is hard to conceive life and motion and all these to omit, eyes, ears, liver, spleen etc. to be contain'd in an insensible particle of matter. Let the anatomist take this animalculum, or a mite (neither of which I suppose he will thinke to be a finer piece of workmanship than the body of a man, or to produce more refined spirits) and when he can but show the parts in one of these insects I shall believe he will be able to show the very operations of those parts in man, and till he does that he does very little towards the discovery of the cause and cure of diseases.

Tis certain, therefore, notwithstanding all our anatomicall scrutinys we are still ignorant, and like to be soe, of the true essential causes of diseases, their manner of production, formalities, and ways of ceasing, and must be much more in the dark as to their cures upon such hypotheses. For supposing it were the acidum amarum et acre of the great Hippocrates, or the sal, sulphur, and mercury, the volat. and the fixd of the chymists that made disorders in the body, and we could

[1] "Demiurge".
[2] "Nature, analogous to the primeval elements of the stars."

come to know which of these in excess it was that produced this malady and where it was lodged, supposing v.g. that too much acid in the bloud or other juices caused the gout, a fever, or epilepsy what indication would this give a practised physician in the cure of either of these diseases. Tis truth twill presently be suggested he must mortifie this acidity but will he be thence enabled to choose fitt remedies, and a due method of their application; will he conclude that pearl, coral, or egg shells, because they take away the acidity in vinegar, will be certain and effectual remedies in the removal of these maladies. He that shall proceed on such grounds as these may indeed constitute fine doctrines, and lay plausible hypotheses, but will not have much to brag of his cures. For the alterations that both our food and physic receives in our mouths, stomachs, guts, glandules etc. are soe many and soe unintelligible to us before they come to the places we design them, that they are quite another thing than we imagine, and work not as we phansie but as nature pleases; and we may as well expect that the juice of wormwood should retain its greenesse or bitternesse in the venae lacteae as any other medicine its naturall qualities till it come to the mass of bloud. For that it is not any sensible qualities by which medicines work their effects on our bodys, and soe cannot by these criterions be chosen and adapted to our hypothesis (all our knowledge of their efficacy being to be acknowledged rather old womens experience than learned mens theories) appears in that wormwood and colcynths are of different uses in physick, that sugar in some stomachs turns to acidity, and milk the most universal and innocent food in the world, is to some men as bad as poison. The anatomist will hardly be enabled to tell us, therefore, what changes any particular medicine either makes or receives in the body, till he can inform us by what artifice, and in what shops, nature makes in the bodys of animalls, volatil salts out of the juice of plants which appear not to have any such substance in them.

TUSSIS[1]

Tussis[2]

A cough which comes from takeing of cold and tends towards a consumption. Method of treatment: A gentle sweat every morning for 14 or more days togeather thus. Take a good draught of sage posset drinke in bed and cover warme and when the patient hath sweat a little give him a dose of Diascord. AE[3] '69, p. 106.

Tussis et Raucedo

Rx. Sem. anis 2 drachms rad. glycyr. pulv. ½ oz. sacchar. cand. rub. 1 oz. mel despumat. in decoct. chinae q.s. f.pil. cap. ½ oz. ter in die hor. medicin. AEs. ib.

Tussis hysterica

Nihil expectorat ib.[4]

Tussis

Method of treatment: tussim ad phthisim tendentem. 1° bleed. 2° purge. 3° binde up mater from falling on the lungs. Rx. conserv. ros. rub. 6 drachms, syr. viol. 1 oz.

Contundantur simul et per setaceum trajiciantur dein adde syr. de meconio 1 oz. sem. papav. alb. aq. ceras. nigr. irrorat. contus. et postea traject. ½ oz. ol. nuc. moschat. per express. 6 grains m. f. ecleg. AE.[5]

Great colds and lasting coughs about Novemb. produce many consumptions the following spring. ib.

There are 3 sorts of coughs tending to a consumption. 1° vernall upon the return of the sun and departure of the cold weather. These come from heat and sharpnesse of the bloud and are the safest of any. Method of treatment: 1° bleed and then cooling and contemperateing. The second sort is when any one being heated lies down on the ground or other wise takes a very great cold. Method of treatment bleeding and sweating. The 3° sort is a great cold taken at the begining of winter at what time the pores being stoped the effluvia of the blood are excreated upon the lungs which by continuance thereof are either

[1] B.L., MS. Locke, c. 42, ff. 258–9.

[2] There are two versions of Sydenham's *Tussis*. One was first arranged as an essay (P.R.O., 30/24/47/2), and later neatly copied into Locke's notebook (B.L., MS. Locke, c. 42) together with sporadic observations before and after the main essay. The earlier essay has been reproduced entirely here, together with Sydenham's additional observations from Locke's notebook. The two sources are indicated in the footnotes.

[3] AE (AEsculapius) was Locke's abbreviation for Sydenham.

[4] Rx. 2 Drachms aniseed, ½ oz. powdered liquorice root, 1 oz. red candied sugar, enough of skimmed honey in decoction of China. Make pills. Take ½ oz. 3 times a day at the usual times for medicine. Aes. ib. Hysteric cough does not cause expectoration. ib.

[5] Rx. 6 drachms conserve of red roses, 1 oz. syrup of violets. Beat together, strain through a cloth. Then add 1 oz. syrup of meconium, ½ oz. of white poppy seeds (moistened in black cherry water, crushed and then strained), 6 grains of oil pressed from nutmegs. Mix and make an eclegma. AE.

ulcerated or soe weakened that the bloud continues this way of evacuation and at last brings on a perfect consumption. They commonly die about May. Method of treatment: cooling incrassateing and stoping the cough. AE. ib.

Tussis Suffocativa Angl. Chin cough

About the midle of Apr. '69 many children were take after this manner. 1° they often fainted without any manifest cause they were also drousy. After they had been thus several days the disease not being yet perfectly formed at length they were taken with a very violent cough with which holding their breath they were almost strangled and would looke black in the face, but did cough up very little. Method of treatment, cooling regimen, frequenting the open aire. Syrop of violet often and whey plentifully taken. Bleeding too would have been useful but the cooling regimen cured without it. Syrop of violets was both cooling and loosening. The cause of this disease was too hot regimen. AE.

All coughs that cause vomiting or reaching to vomit are to be cured by bleeding 2 or 3 times repeated as there shall be occasion and also decoctum pectorale and barly water with reasons and liquirish and diet (without flesh and wine) espetially if it be the hooping or chin cough. AE. ib.

Tussis virginea

Want or suppression of the menses in virginibus at due season often brings with the green sickenesse a cough tending to a consumption. Method of treatment, 1° bleed at that time of the moon when the matter seems to have a tendency to that evacuation, next day repeat bleeding which is to be repeated at the same revolution of the moon, 2 or 3 times if there be occasion and in the meane time decoctum pectorale AE '69, p. 107.

TUSSIS[1]

A cough is a symptom attending some disaffection of the lungs immediately, but primarily of the bloud which according to the severall ways of the blouds being distemperd may be distinguished into severall sorts.

1°

In that time of the yeare which is between spring and summer the bloud being by the constitution of the yeare put as it were into a new and livelyer fermentation, it doth (in those whose lungs by any weaknesse are disposd to receive impressions from the bloud) in its passage through the lungs either by steames riseing from it, or some hot and sharpe particles in it irritate the lungs and soe provoke to coughing. This vernall ebullition of the bloud if it prove very high grows perfectly febrile and begins as other fevers doe with a rigor and horror, and soe after some little continuance makes its self a vent into the lungs by a

[1] P.R.O., 30/24/47/2, ff. 31–4 verso.

downright hemaptoe. Infants and contrarywise persons that are ancient are seldome troubled with this. Those of the midle age when endowd with thin hot tender and loose habits of body are in the time of the yeare before mentiond most liable to it and are sensible both before the coming on thereof and likewise dureing the same of a heate and tendernesse in the upper parts of their breasts, and have likewise ever now and then a glowing and transient heat in their hands feet and divers parts of their bodys espetially their cheekes. <At the first comeing on of this cough they spit up noething, the steams that irritate the lungs being as they are excretd in upon the lungs sufficiently evacuatd by respiration, but after some continuance of the cough when the lungs come to be weakend, then they usually expectorate in the morning soe much as hath been spewd into the lung out of the bloud dureing the precedent night. This by degrees when not cured as well as all tother species of coughs hereafter to be mentioned by debilitating the lungs to such a degree that they are not able to concoct their own nourishment throws the patient into a perfect phthisis wherein all the signes attending it doe show themselves.> Besides which and the cough its self I have not observd any other appearances peculiar to the disease but to the haemoptoe febricitation somewhat more intense doth likewise belong and consequently from the inflammation of the bloud greater in this than the other the bloud when taken is puriforme as in pleuritis.

The cure of Tussis verna

As to this cough which I call Tussis Verna[1] other curative intentions are to be directed to these 2 points: the contempering and incrassateing of the bloud.

1° day bleed moderatly the next day purge. Then use the following: Rx. conser. ros. rub. et syr. viol. $\overline{an}$ 1 oz. contundantur simul in mortar et per setaceum trajiciantur deinde adde syr de meconnio $1\frac{1}{2}$ ozs. sem papav. alb aq. ceras. nigror irrorat. et contus. et per setaceum traject.[2] ol. nuc. mosch. per express. gr. iiij. f. eclegma de quo lambat saepe saepius praecipue urgente tussi.[3]

Rx. sem melon pepon. et papav. alb $\overline{an}$ $\frac{1}{2}$ oz. contundantur in mortario sensim affundendo aq. ceras. nigror 12 ozs. sacchar cand. alb. 6 drachms m. f. emulsio cap 3 ozs. ter vel quater in die.[4] The patient is to

[1] Locke first wrote "Florida", then "Calida per se", finally "Verna".

[2] Bodley MS. adds here "3 drachms".

[3] Rx. 1 oz. each of conserve of red roses and syrup of violets. Beat together in a mortar, and strain through a cloth. Then add $1\frac{1}{2}$ ozs. syrup of meconium, 3 drachms white poppy seeds (moistened in black cherry water, crushed and strained through a cloth), 4 grains of oil pressed from nutmegs. Make an eclegma. Let him sip this as often as he likes, especially when the cough is troublesome.

[4] Rx. $\frac{1}{2}$ oz. each of seeds of ripe melons and seeds of white poppy. Beat in a mortar, gradually pouring on 12 ozs. of black cherry water and 6 drachms of white candied sugar. Mix. Make an emulsion. Take 3 ozs. 3 or 4 times a day.

forbeare use of flesh and strong drinks instead of which barley water is to be given. If the time of the yeare shall be a little advanced from the spring or the comeing of the disease approach an haemoptoe a bath of moderately warme water used once a day for 6 days will alone doe the businesse above all other remedies.[1]

<Another sort of cough there is incident to children which comes on sometimes before the vernall equinox which is vulgarly called hooping or chine cough wherein the patient expectorates litle but is taken with a long continued act of coughing which rises higher and higher both in the straining and hooping noise untill at length the child grows black sometimes bleeds at the nose and foams at the mouth through the violence thereof.

This cough being occasiond by a great impulse of the bloud upon the vessells of the lungs the curative intentions are to be directed only to revulsions and accordingly the child is to be blouded 1°, and afterwards purged upon which by degrees the cough will goe off without any more adoe save that it may be necessary to let it use the open country aire.>[2]

2° Tussis pituitosa

In winter espetialy that part thereof which approacheth the winter solstice, the bloud being filled with a large proportion of cold and phlegmatick humors suitable to the time of the yeare doth usualy to give some vent to them and ease its self of this load, discharge them either upon the lungs immediately by the branches of the arteria pulmonalis, or else evacuating this humor by the glandules about the throat cause a distillation upon the lungs or the larynges, and by that irritation provoke coughing. This sort of cough though none be exempt from it, yet doth most familiarly seise children who are naturally full of pituitous humors, or else grosse and phlegmatique persons espetialy such as indulge to a[3] sedentary life. From the very first beginning of the blouds dischargeing its self, there is a plentifull expectoration, if it begin with a cough, for some times the bloud makeing its first way by the glandules of the nose and those more remot from the larynx the first appearance is in a defluxion on those parts and sometimes where the caus is great a gravedo, which commonly terminate also in this sort of cough. This defluxion in the beginning is constantly thin, how plentifully soever the matter be discharged, but after 4 days or thereabouts it begins to come to concoction and grow thicker and the patient feels some feverish heate in his outward parts, the urin is high and turbid with a gravelly sediment in the bottom. In some persons who are very phlegmatique and doe use the free aire

[1] Bodley MS. adds the reference "AE '69, p. 182".
[2] *Ibid.* adds the reference "AE ib.".
[3] *Ibid.* has "indulge a too sedentary".

and indulge not to the use of strong liquors the discharge is perfectly thin and pituitous dureing the whole time of the cough but in persons of more sanguin and robust constitutions who keep them selves hot and tenderly and that drinke strong liquors and take hot medecins the matter bakes up sooner and stuffes the passages of the lungs, from which and a great inflammation upon all the spirituall parts the cough is made which I call Tussis callida per accidens,[1] wherein the great violence of fits of coughing accompanid with straining and almost tearing of the lungs straitness of the breast great pains in the head ready as they call it to split their brains doth at last when they are ready to sinke for want of breath end in vomiting.

Tussis pituitosa

The curative indications are to be directed to the lessening the pituitous matter in the bloud and the obviating accidents attending the discharge. As to the first lying a bed and keepeing in a warme roome contributes to the takeing away that phlegmatique disposition in the bloud, but if the patient be either stronge or other wise hath passed the first 4 days and begins to be feverish the open fresh aire is to be taken more plentifully than before it was to be avoided. As to the 2^{d} the great accident to be obviated is the bakeing up of the pituitous matter too soon and the intending the heat which attends it too much, in order to which strong liquors espetially any strong wine or vinous spirits are to be avoided being those things with which an infinite number of people have destroid them selves in stead whereof the ordinary liquor which the patient used in his health with the addition only of actuall heat is to be given and some moderate pectorall not too highly attenuateing is to be given. That this accidentall heat may not come on upon the account of the matters being not freely discharged, oyl of sweet almonds is beyond all comparison the best of this sort it being a well concocted medecin. This also I use: Rx. decocti pectoralis 12 ozs. croci in nodulo ligat ½ drachm syr. e capil veneris 3 ozs. cap 4 ozs. ter in die tepide.[2] ⟨Were this cough comes on every winter and is attended with an asthma in aged men the advance of the summer only can cure it for that season and it will returne next winter.⟩

Tussis Calida per Accidens

But now if it hath baked up the accidents attending tussis calida per accidens are come on the curative indications are to be altred and to be directed to the takeing downe of the heat and in a manner to the bringing on a new rawnesse as it were upon the bloud to which purpose 1° bleed, purge next day, and soe 3 times alternis diebus intermixing the pectorall decoction without safron addeing syr

[1] Bodley MS. adds the reference "AE '69, p. 183".

[2] Rx. 12 ozs. pectoral decoction, ½ drachm of crocus tied in a bundle, 3 ozs. of syrup of maidenhair. Take 4 ozs. warm thrice a day.

viol. et capill ven an̄ 2½ ozs. and syr de meconio[1] each night after purgeing.[2]

It[3] was said before that when the lungs have been long debilitated by any of those coughs that there is a danger of a phthisis, in which state the cough haveing run with ease a great diuturnity and being sometimes crude and some times concoctd without any setled order it is then altogeather in vain to expect a remedy from any medecins that I yet know, for in this case the curative intention being to be directd to the strengthening of the bloud soly, and noe medecins doeing the same that doe not heat and at the same time irritate the cough this indication can be satisfied by noe other way in my opinion than by rideing which, being persisted in some months togeather, will I am sure cure any thing beneath the highest degree of a downright phthisis. For by churneing the bloud and puteing the severall excretory parts upon performing their functions the bloud at length arrives to that perfect condition which can possibly be incident to the primogeniall constitution and age of the patient, for if we doe consider how many 1000 succussions of the body, and that in a free aire, are made in one day what humor can we suppose to be soe stubborne but this exercise if persisted it must discusse, what purulent matter or other substance but it must qua data porta through off and what naturall heat soe languid but it must excite to help all off. Never the lesse these cautions must be observed generall evacuations must be made before the exercise be ingaged on. The patient must be injoynd to ride gently at first and to increase his journey by litle and litle untill he be able to perform an ordinary day's journey which must be uninterruptedly continued untill he has perfectly recovered his health observing all this while noe diet but such as is most gratefull to him.[4]

There are other species incident to all times of the yeare indifferently the most considerable of which I shall here recite. The chiefest of which is that which happens in depuratory years which is most incident to young persons, and, for the most part, comes upon this occasion, the patient having heated himself with exercise and afterwards taken cold either by lying on the cold ground or leaving off some accustomd clothes, is suddenly seized on with a rigor and horror succeeded with a fever of that season which presently, is terminated with a violent cough, the cough indeed being noething else than the fever invertd which no longer appears a fever, but exercises however its tragedies

[1] 2½ ozs. each of syrup of violets and maidenhair and syrup of meconium.
[2] Bodley MS. adds the reference: "'69, p. 184".
[3] *Ibid.* has here the marginal title "Phthisis".
[4] *Ibid.* adds the reference "'69, p. 184".

in another appearance and doth that in some months which the other would have done in a few days.

[In the margin opposite this paragraph Sydenham has written: "Here the cures done by riding are to be brought in reference to the cure of consumptions and morbi obscuri."]

This is the great consumption of mankinde in respect not soe much of the number of those that are attaqued there with. For as to that the other two kindes are as frequent to wit those that doe depend upon debilitations, and those that doe depend upon ulcers from pleurisys peripneumonias or any other hurt of the lungs. But in respect of the greatness of the symptoms which at the very first appear to be both by the looke of the patient and all other signes the very same (excepting that of the diarrhaea syntectica which comes not on till the end as well in this as the rest) with the most adult symptoms of the other two. I have not observed this to come on in any other than depuratory years.

The curative scope must be directed not to the cough but to the fever and accordingly the patient managed in all respects as in a depuratory fever viz 1° bleeding, then vomiting, giveing a clyster every other day till 11th day and then to give cordialls till 14th, then 17th day to purge keepeing the patient all this while in his bed with a fire in the roome and prohibiting flesh, and soe to recon from the time you bleed.[1]

Another sort of cough is that which doth proceed from hurts of the lungs that end in abscesses as pleurisys not well carried off but ending in Empyemas in which the matter haveing through neglect caused such impostumation, bleeding which before would have prevented this mischiefe, now comes too late and indeed makes that which is the only cure of such impostumations dangerous, to wit the use of minerall purgeing waters which alone constantly persisted in, cures this disease when as hath been said bleeding hath not been used or very spareingly and a good while before.[2,3]

f. 264 Tussis Suffocativa

To cure the hooping cough. 1° bleed. Then purge 5 or 6 days togeather. This cough is from something in the bloud that puts the lungs into convulsion. It seldome kills anybody. ib. AE.

[1] Bodley MS. adds the reference "'69, p. 185, AE".
[2] *Ibid.* adds the reference "ib, 186, AE".
[3] The text of P.R.O., 30/24/47/2 ends here. The remaining paragraph is only in B.L., MS. Locke, c. 42, f. 264.

SMALLPOX, 1669

[Dedicated to the first Earl of Shaftesbury.]

Ep[*istle*][1]

I know he takes but an ill way of gratitude and makes but ill use of the favour of a great man who ventures to prefix his name to a lie and desires the patronage of a noble person to gain credit to a falsehood and make it passe the more unquestionable in the world. This consideration alone, had I noe regard to truth, conscience, and the lives of men, would make me very wary how, after the many favours I have received from your lordship and the trust you have reposed in me, I returnd you such an affront to your lordship and made you an accomplice in a cheat of no lesse a concernment than the lives of men, by publishing to the world under your protection the cure of a disease dangerous and fatall to those who shall by my professions be tempted to make use of it. The world knows you are too wise a man easily to be imposed upon and am sure you are too great a man safely to be provoked by such an imposture, and were I not by long and reitratd experience confirmd in the certainty of what I here publish, it would not become me to engage your lordships name in a controversy (for soe it is now become) which if I had beene as forward hot by noise and clamour to maintain, as others by reproaches, false reports, secret and open defamation have been hot to prosecute and decry, had by this time grown into a faction. It fares not always soe well with Truth and Right as not to need a patronage, new truths espetially such as stand in the way of receivd maxims and generall practice, and like trees sprouting up in the midst of the beaten road, which however usefull or pleasant if not fenced whilst they are young and defended till they are growne to [*sic*] sturdy for common injury, are sure to be tramped on in the bud and to be trod into dust and forgetfulnesse. The doctrine and method I here set forth is something of that nature. All that in their following this disease go the usuall road are apt to spurn it. It will need your lordships protection soe long till the world sees what fruit it bears and if upon triall they find it not safe and sallutary I shall willingly consent your lordship withdraw your protection from it and leave it and the author to that scorne and contempt which he shall deserve who trifles with the lives of men, or out of a perverse and disingenious obstinate persisting in adhesion to an old error or a new mistake, for

[1] P.R.O., 30/24/47/2, ff. 50–2.

both are equally dangerous, shall with great assurance persuade them to their distruction, and under the pretence of cureing them put them upon the most hazardous and deadly practise and by this means murder men at a distance. In the meane time it will not I hope appear a very unreasonable request if I desire to shelter my selfe a little while till triall can be made under your Lordships care from the obloquie has attended me for endeavouring to doe my country and age service, wherein I presume I have not been unsuccessfull, at least I must be allowed to deal soe candidly and fairly in this matter, that I put it to an easy triall and doe not by any hidden arcanums or conceald medicins, pretend to doe wonders, and thereby gain admiration and custome, a way which however suspitious in its self yet I have observd many others to practise, not only without clamour and disturbance, but even with applause and approbation, though many times those cried up preparations have produced fatal effects and most commonly very uncertain cures in the credulous takers. I say not this to undervalue the medicins of other men, but only to let your Lordship see how difficultly it has fared with me, who have under gone soe many rebukes and reproaches in the prosecution of a plain and open method, which I never indeavoured, nor indeed could conceal from anyone who had but the curiosity to observe it, and which I thinke had noe fault unless some men will think it one to be plaine and easy and such as poor people may, to the saving their lives, make use of without the help of a physitian. But my Lord I ought not to hold your Lordship to long with this story. I confess I have many great obligations to your Lordship and am not so misled by common custom to imagine I pay any part of them by this dedication unlesse it be some kind of acknowledgment to witness to the world that I believe your Lordship soe great a patriot that in the high station you are in you will not think it unworthy your care to look after the lives of your country men and to preserve them as well from home bred diseases and foreign invasions, his majesty and your country suffering equally in both by the loss of mens lives. At least my Lord I thought it reasonable to let your Lordship see that I have practised noething in your family but what I durst owne and publish to the world, and let my country men see that I tell them noething here but what I have already tried with noe ill successe on severall in the family of one of the greatest and most eminent personages among them.

Praef [*ace*][1]

Reader,

I heare present thee with a history and cure of a disease which however but too well knowne both by its terrible aspect and fatall effects

[1] P.R.O., 30/24/47/2, ff. 54–61.

to most familys in England, yet as to the true state of the disease and the right method of ordering of it has hitherto laine in obscurity and the true cure hath been soe far from the ordinary practice that the very report of it hath made a great noise, and it has not scaped without the charge of a bold innovation. I say not this with disrespect to the physitians of former ages, nor reproach to the doctor of this. I know what is to be allowd to prepossession and education, receivd opinions I confess how false so ever, backed with generall uncontrold practice are not easily to be removed out of the mindes of men. And I quarell not with others for following their own maxims and methods, but yet must take the liberty to vindicate myself from the scandels and calumnys, which the doeing my duty and dealing with my patients as became an honest and conscientious man hath drawn upon me. Perhaps I had done more advantageously for myself and had without doubt better securd my owne Interest and fame if I had followed the old tract. I could without much pains have directed cordialls my self or transcribed them out of bookes. It was noe hard matter to have prescribd warmth and sweating and amidst the use of a great many comfortable things to have suffered my patient to have lived or died with great reputation. In which way of proceeding with little care and thoughtfullness I might securely have advanced my credit and profit, whilst the recovery of a patient dangerously ill, plied with store of spetious remedys suited to the common opinion had been sure by the friends and by standers, to have been looked on as the effect of my skill, and his death charged on the malignity of the disease not to be overcome by the most powerfull remedys. If, therefore, I had regarded ease and fame, Sennertus or Riverius, or almost any practitioner extant, would in this case have directed me quietly to it; I needed not have troubled my head with pensive thoughts and great labour of minde, to seek out a more effectuall method. When in the old way, however, my patient miscaried my esteem reputation and credit stood safe and unshaken. Whereas in this bold undertaking I am to contest not only the disease, but most commonly, what is more uncurable, the prejudices of Relations and Assistants, the skill of over wise nurses and the receivd practice of physitians, and after all when my patient without danger and very little sicknesse has passed through the course of this troublesome disease and is arrived at perfect health it is by many lookd on but as a happy event of a rash undertaking, or the escape has been imputed to the favourablenesse of the disease, or the patients good and robust constitution who could not be kild by an irregular and unsuitable treatment. So hard is it by plain and visible effects to convince those who possessed by prejudices will not allow anything to be true which may thwart with the opinions they have been bred up in, and take it amiss to have their friends curd as much as to be cloakd out of the fashion. But if some of those (for the sober and considerate have been content to believe their eyes) who have seen this disease treated in my way have yet had doubtfull thoughts about it, how much has my rashnesse and ignorance been exploded by those who haveing barely heard of my keeping my patients coole in the small pox yet neither knew me nor the success of my method. How have the good ladies been offended that I have slighted their cordialls and would not suffer the children of those who were committed to my care to die as their friends and relations had done heretofore. What storys of extravagancy and folly have the talk of prejudicd people brought upon me, soe much that it has been told to persons of quality that I have taken those who have had the small pox out of their beds and put them into cold water. How much some of my own faculty have fomented and increasd these reports they themselves know and with what design I leave it to their owne consciences to tell them only they must give me leave to say it would have become them out of common charity as good men, as well as out of an obligation to improve their art and save mens lives as physitians, upon the first intimation of an unusuall method of cureing so common a disease as this is, to have enquired more particularly of the way, observd the circumstances, and informd themselves of the events, before they had cried it down as dangerous and fatall, and frightened all that came within their reach from an enquiry into or triall of this method by the abhorrency they had given them against so bold and hazardous a practice.

For if the way I here publish be upon examination found (as I doubt not but it will) safe and secure, free not only from danger but even sicknesse too; I fear the world will have reason to suspect that they have not that regard to truth nor that tendernesse for the health of men which befits those who professe to take care of it, and that they value not how many mens lives are sacrificied to their method and maxims, soe the reputation of their learning and their owne ways of practise be but secured. I should not make these reflections, how true soever, had I not been used by some of them with these greatest indignitys beyond almost the suffrance of a man to the endangering not only of my reputation and lively hood but even my life its self which may well deserve to be questiond if as some have reportd by unallowable practices I doe soe certainly indanger and destroy my patients. But I chalenge them and al men living to produce one instance where one patient of mine sick of the small pox being ordered my way has miscarried. Tis true sometimes when either the prejudice of friends would not suffer me to treat my patients in a way to which they were averse and sometimes when the frequent discourses have been had of me as a rash and venturous or a senseless and ignorant man came to my ears (nay I have been told even by physitians that this has been no less than a particular madnesse) I have been at a stand in my owne thoughts, distrusted my owne experience and out of a desire to avoid singularity and perpetuall contention have returned again to the old method of cureing this disease wherein if my patients have sometimes died under my care it ought to be charged upon hot keepeing and cordialls and the method in fashion and not to be mentioned to disgrace the contrary way of cure which has never failed to be successful and which hereafter I cannot with a safe conscience forsake or discard whenever I shall be cald to any sick of this disease, however desperate this method may appear to others or prove prejudiciall to my self, who am not to neglect the cure of my patient intrusted to me and of whose life I am to give an account, nor deviate from that way which I know to be best upon any so mean a consideration as quick fame or the opinion of others. This alone hath brought me into the noise and talk of the world, and I have not without foresight of it, incurd the severe censures I have fallen under in defence only of my patients lives and that truth I am sure posterity will thank me for. For it was not a forward affectation of novelty and opposition that made me run headlong upon this condemnd course, nor any desire to follow melancholy by paths of my owne findeing amidst thorns and bryars made me forsake the common road, but finding that notwithstanding the most diligent attendance and careful use of the choisest cordialls many, of not only mine, but other physitians patients miscarried in the small pox and many more very narrowly escaped, and were weak for a long time after. I thought it a very uncomfortable practice where notwithstanding the best method I could propose or saw used, the patient being governable and the assistants diligent, I could yet with noe assurance to myself or hopes to my patient undertake the cure which would be very doubtfull in the event. I first therefore bethought myself whether the sweats usually prescribed and prosecuted in the beginning might not be prejudiciall in a disease the discharge whereof Nature had designed in another way by pustles and little imposthumes. The first thing, therefore, that I decided on towards the cureing of this disease was the cuting off and preventing these sweats, which attempts had no ill successe but yet was not enough wholy to secure my patient. The next step therefore was to abate in great measure the plenty of cordialls that used to be given in the small pox, which I did but by slow degrees, for though the very nature of the disease being in it self very hot and feverish and very apt on every occasion to break out with great burning might to any observing person seem little to need such heating remedys yet my inclination to the old opinion and practice kept me long in the use of them and twas late before I left them quite off, which I retained till my dayly experience as I forebore their use gave me new incouragement the more to forebeare them and that I found that those people always underwent this disease with least sicknesse and danger who took the least of them, and were most removed from hot keepeing either by clothes on their bodys or fire in their room. But findeing that in the heat of summer in people of high and sanguin constitutions and a flox pox, bare abstaining from heat and hot medicins was not enough to preserve my patient from very ill accidents and great danger soe long as I kept them in bed, I had at last venturd to make them rise wherein they found such present relief that some that have been languishing and ready to die in their beds, have upon their riseing immediately found alteration in their strength and pulse and thought themselves instantly recoverd by it. But to perfect the cure there was one thing more yet requird which I found not till this summer when through the heat of the weather or a particular constitution of the yeare the pox was in many apt to turn black and there would appear blew spots upon the skin where in few that were kept moderately warme and with the ordinary remedys escaped. I found it therefore necessary in these actually to cool them not only by rising and wearing very thin clothes, but by giving them whey which for severall days together was the only physick or food they tooke. And by these slow steps has it beene that after long and pensive thoughts about the small pox I have in many yeares beene able to perfect the cure of this disease which besides the good successe that usually attends it, has this advantage over other methods, that the patient after the third or fourth day when the pox begins to come out has not any fever or other sicknesse dureing the whole course of the disease and saving the pain which is occasiond by the swelling of the face and other parts and the soarnesse of the pustles is as well as at any other time of his life which of its self is noe small argument that this is the genuin and naturall cure of the disease.

If it were necessary to raise theorys, and from thence draw probable arguments to prove that to be likely which is already veryfied in matter of fact and experience has justified to be true, the method I make use of in cureing this disease is as capable of a fair defence and may be made out from as rationall grounds as the cure of any disease whatsoever. He that shall well consider the hystory of this disease in all its circumstances and symptoms will finde reason to imagine that hot medicins and management may not be very agreeable to its safe cure for this is a disease properly of the spring, grows up with the heat and warmth of the yeare and is most severe and mortall in the sultriest part of summer. If therefore heat by the opening of the pores and provoking transpiration served well to carry off the vesicules, and, as it is cald, malignant matter, and by that means to discharge the disease we might well espect milder symptoms and safer events at a season when the temper of the aire most contributed to its genuine cure by opening passages of the skin and calling out the cause and occasion of all the disorder within. Whether this be soe I appeal to experience and perhaps it will be found hereafter noe false nor inconsiderable observation that few or none of the diseases whose proper time of breaking out is in the spring when the bloud is of it self strong and vigorous and little needs to be inflamed by cordiall are to be curd by a hot regimen or heating medicins, which are apt to disturb other regular motions of nature, increase the disorder and by confounding the humors hinder the work she is about.

It is a disease of many sanguin people, and as it commonly soe it most dangerously seises those who are full of heat and spirit in the flourishing part of their age, and as it were the spring of their lives, and whose nature and constitution has already provided soe great strength and warmth of bloud. Where the heart is soe vigorous, and the spirits naturally soe unruly and apt to take harm and break out into disorder, one would suppose there were little need to add fuell to the fire. *Vinum et iuventus duplex incendium.*[1] Who finds not that wine is very prejudiciall in most people till they are past the acme of their age and very apt to inflame the bloud and produce dangerous fevers. Who would to a young man in the small pox already too hot with his owne temper and the burning of the disease think it convenient to give him sack and strong bere or season all he takes with peper and cloves, for what I pray are all the cordialls that are given to expel this disease but either the strong and spirituous parts of wine drawn to geather by distillation, or the aromaticall parts of vegetables unitd into some composition, and by these ways of preparation made only hotter more displeasing to the palat and more remote from the grateful nature of food and soe disguisd into physick. For I ask any man why canary its self or muscadine is not a better cordiall more pleasing to the taste and stomach wherein besides the spirituous vinous parts, which alone are the cordiall, there is in its naturall composition a very delicate and gratefull realish not easily to be made by art, why I say, are not those better given them selves, than when by distillation they be turnd into Brandy though by the addition of different but hot ingredients they are

[1] "Wine and youth both start a conflagration."

diversified into severall magnified cordiall waters and weare the gaudy names of aq. Epidemica, aq. Theriacalis stillat whereof there are an infinit number amongst all which I imagin there is to be found in reference to their use in the small pox, and all other diseases, noe other difference but their strength and relish. As to their taste there are very few that will not thinke the naturall wines them selves much better, but are not to be prescribed because they look not soe much like physick, and there is not sufficient appearance of art and learning in it, and if these cordiall waters are weaker, that is lesse hot and venous than sack or muscadine, why such pains to prepare them when smaller wines or diluted would better serve the turne. And if they are stronger certainly in this hot and feverish disease which never was, nor will be, cured by sweat or transpiration, they are certainly much worse. Is it not ridiculous to see the grave old gentlewoman or the experienced nurse forbid the touching a drop of strong beare or wine in the small pox for feare it should augment the heat and give a dangerous increase to the feaver, and yet at the same time, give him the hotter and more inflaming spirits of those very liquors distild into brandy and prescribd by the doctor under the name of a cordiall and expect from this that the cause of the distemper should be breathed out and the poor young gent be made cooler who perhaps got this distemper and inflamed his bloud into the small pox by drinking wine or the same sort of brandy. If therefore there were any indication for such strong liquors in this case, would not wine its self be better to which probably the patient haveing been accustomd in the time of his health his stomach would better receive a liquor that was familiar to it and which by its naturall crasis is better suited to refresh us than when that gratefull taste is destroyd by distillation and cannot by any mixtures or artifice of ours be recoverd again. It is plain therefore by their owne confession, and their condemning strong beare and wine, ordinary and familiar cordiall drinks, and those very liquors from which the others are drawn, that they think and finde by experience that hot and vinous liquors are dangerous and hurtfull in the small pox, and thereby seem to expect the good effects they promise them selves by the use of cordialls from some specific qualitys in the ingredients or composition, and does not primarily and immediately consist in that heat which they cause in the bloud when taken. But I would gladly know from any one what one specifick cordiall produces any effect in our bodys and operates any other way then a draught of good wine doth. Almost all the cordialls used in this disease being either parts of animals and vegetables (the purely minerall used being few and I think of not undoubtd efficacy) both which are noe otherwise cordiall then as they abound with either hot oyle or volatil salts both which when put into our bloud are apt to produce in it a great ebullition, the effects whereof are heat, and in bodys disposed to it, sweat. And thus in short a greater ebullition fomentation or volatilization of the bloud, or what ever you call it, where of heat and a brisker circulation is alway the concomitant, is the proper and immediate effect of cordialls, and what soever is apt to excite that flamma vitalis or igniculus cordis is rankd with that classis. Now of those there are two sorts: first vegetable which consists in noething but great plenty of a volatil oyl separable from the concret by distillation, wherein spices abounding more than other principles usually carry the first rank among cordialls, and being by virtue of their hot oyle very apt to inflame the bloud, and as it were adde new and very combustible matter to it, are lookd upon as very comfortable things and apt to strengthen the heart and raise the spirits; of which rank also are angelica zedoary balm and such herbs as abounds in volatil oyle. And that their chief efficacy lyes in exciting the effervescence of the bloud by their hot oyly parts is obvious to any who considers that their ordinary distilld waters haveing by that way of preparation very little of this oyle mixd with them have very little efficacy in strengthening the vitals or disposeing the body to sweat or a freer diaphoresis, and he who shall take large quantitys of these, as the chymists calls them phlegms, will not finde himselfe much warmed or revivd by them and may sooner expect to be put into a sweat by warm possett drinke then by larger quantitys of borage or buglos water however esteemd cordiall they be if the actuall heat of them be not made use of to produce it.[1]

Sagacissimi viri et practici faelicissi[mi] D^{ni} D^{ris} Thomae Sydenham amici sui plurimum Colendi tractatus de Variolis an̄. 1669.[2]

The Small pox of all other diseases is the most common, as that which sooner or later (at least in this part of the world) attaques most men. When it proves very epidemicall it comes in about that time of the yeare which comprehends the end of the spring and the begining of summer, and usually runs out in great vigor till the returne of the nexte yeare, leaveing likewise some scatterings of it self even through out an other yeare. There are only two sorts of the true pox: viz Distinct & Flox of which I shall here treat, omiting to mention any sort of the illegitimate ones, they being many and very different.

[1] The preface is obviously unfinished.

[2] B.L., MS. Locke, c. 21, ff. 3–17. The title reads: "The Treatise on Smallpox, dated 1669, of the author's very good friend and master, Dr. Thomas Sydenham, a man of great learning, and a most successful practitioner."

First the Destinct ones invade for the most part with a rigor and horror which are succeeded with a great heat, pain in the head and back, a reaching to vomit, a great tendernesse in the parts under the scrobiculus cordis when pressed with the hand, a great aptitude to sweat provided the patient be adult; these are the most ordinary symptoms that attend the invasion of this disease. Others there are less ordinary, as a great dosinesse and disposition to sleepe, a flux of the belly, convulsion fits when the patient is a childe and many more. But upon the eruption which most commonly in this sort of pox happens to be on the fourth day, sometimes after, but very seldome before, there is wont to be in proportion to their comeing forth a palliation of these, and all other symptoms, and at length (the disposition to sweat only excepted this still continueing) a totall cessation of them, the patient finding himself well and in as good a condition as if he ailed noe thing. First little red spots noe bigger than small pins heads begin to show themselves here and there, first upon the face most commonly or about the neck or bosome, and afterwards upon the whole body. These growing biger and riseing higher every day doe by degrees draw the adjacent flesh in the interstitia into rednesse and inflammation, and about the eighth day, the face proportionably to the number of pustles that beset it, is red and begins to swell up, the patient feeling therein a painfull drubing and shooting at this time, but in the progresse of the disease the palpebrae are very often soe stretched with inflammation that he is not able to looke abroad till about this day, the pustles have continued smooth to the touch of ones finger and red, but from thence forward they begin to be roughish to the touch (which is the very first indicium of their being comeing to maturity) and likewise to be at least upon their heads of a yellowish colour like an honey comb. Those on the face grow more rugged and yellow every day thereafter till they scale off. But those on the hands and the rest of the body are lesse rugged and grow whiter. Those of the face and the rest of the body goe off by scaleing, those on the hands by breaking. Those of the face and rest of the body are usually dried up and gon by the fourteenth or fifteenth day but those on the hands remain green a good while after. In the place of those on the face a certain scurfe comes on which makes way for the piting. For upon the first shelling noe uneavennesse in the skin appears. But afterwards the scurfe successively comes and goes till the pits are made which we see. Though notwithstanding tis to be observed that this sort of pox how large and full soever when it happens at any time between Christmas and midsomer leaves not any impression which disfigures the face as doth very often those of the contrary season of the yeare. Dureing the whole disease the body is either altogeather bound or the patient goes but very seldome to stoole. Thus much for the Destinct pox.

Secondly, The flox pox invade in the like manner as the other doe save that now and then they begin with a great pain about the region of the kidneys resembling a nephriticall paroxysme and more rarely with a pain in the side like a pleurisy either of which ways of invadeing shew that they will prove a very high flox. But invade how they will their eruption most commonly happens to be the third day sometimes before but never after. And by how much sooner they appeare than that time by soe much more they flox. They come forth sometimes like an Erysipelas and sometimes like the measles from which he must be a very experiensed physitian that can destinguish them and though a cough when attending such eruptions may render it probable that they will prove the measles, yet that doth not always hold. They rise not up in progresse of time to any considerable bulke espetially on the face as the destinct ones doe, but catching hold of one another are first all over like one continued blister and swell the face as much or more than the other, but are afterwards like one continual white skin pasted on to the face and riseing not very high above the true superficies of the same. About the eighth or ninth or tenth day, the said white skin begins in some places to feele rough to the touch and from that time growes not of a yellow but browne colour and dayly increases in those two qualitys till it begins to fall off in broad fleaks, which in some parts of the face may not now and then happen in above twenty days. The shelling off of these likewise leaves noe uneaveanesse in the face at first but is succeeded with a scurfe that is of a very corrodeing nature, and doth not only at any time of the yeare whatsoever pit more than the other before mentioned but likewise endangers scauring. If it be a very high flox the cuticula will peale off in many places of the body as on the neck, shoulders and back and leave the subjacent parts raw. But all this while it constantly happens in this sort of pox that the patient if adult hath been troubled with a ptyalisme wherein the matter comes first thin and continues easy to be brought up till about the eleventh day, at what time it is very viscouse and hard to excreat. But if he be an infant he hath had a Diarrhoea nature having providently found out one of these two ways for the discharge of that matter which in these depressed pox could not be had equal with what is found in those other elevated ones before mentioned.

This disease in its self is very salutary and when not mishandled kills few or none, nature haveing annexed thereunto both a full and convenient discharge of the morbifick matter.

This is the naturall history of the small pox as comprehending the true and genuine phaenomina belonging to them as they are in their owne nature, but other anomalous accidents there are which attend the disease when unduely managed and that create very great danger to the patient. Of these I shall now treat.

Tis to be noted therefor that amongst all the anomalous accidents those which occur the eighth day in the destinct pox and the eleventh in the Flox, still reconing from the invasion, deserve the chiefest consideration in regard it will appeare (a thing which hither to hath not been sufficiently observed) that most who die of either of these two sorts of small pox die in one of the two days respectively. For first in the Destinct pox the unskilfull physitian findeing in the patient a great propension to sweat (which as hath been said is very incident to all adult persons in the small pox) and promiseing to himself great advantage in his businesse from breatheing out the malignityes (as he calls it) of the disease he carefully provides that the same be cherished, both by giveing cordialls and ordering a hot regimen suitable to the same. And this he doth soe much the rather because he findes the patient very well at first under this management, besides the compliance it beares with the weake conceptions of the bystanders as well as his owne. But at length the parts which should contribute both to the riseing of the pustles and the swelling of the face being by such sweats discharged, it comes to passe that the eighth day the face which at that time should begin to swell and inflame in the interstitia between the eruptions is contrary wise lanke and the said interstitia are white, though yet the pustles themselves are red and stand up high even to the very last. The sweat which till now hath been kept up on a suddain vanisheth of its owne accord and is not to be recald by the use of any cordialls how hot soever, the patient grows phreneticall, hath great inquietude, complains of great sicknesse, makes water in great quantitys very often, and in a little time after dies. But neverthelesse tis to be noted that where the small pox are but very few, the time of the yeare winter, the patient is ancient and hath been blouded, the hot keepeing before mentioned doth not soe certainly inferre this danger of the faces not swelling and consequently the death of the patient, as where the pox are many, the season of the yeare spring or summer, the patient is young or hath lost noe bloud, and I doubt not but the recovery of some one or more under the former circumstances, though thus unduely managed, hath beene the death of many a man in the like manner treated under contrary circumstances espetially those of spring and youth to which two this danger is more espetially incident.

But now in the flox pox the day of the greatest danger and wherein most die is eleventh from the invasion for the matter of the ptyalisme which till now was crude thin and easy to bring up is at this time become viscouse and baked up: by which means the patient is in danger of being suffocated, hath a dozeing upon him, and labours under a great stupidity, the parts being clogd and loaden, in which agony he often times dies. Though as I have said before, this accident of a ptyalisme is naturall to adult persons in the flox pox, yet that the matter thereof should bake up to such a degree as to cause the dire symptoms here mentioned, is very unnaturall, and what would not happen if the patient were moderately kept.

Other accidents there are which occur at any time of the small pox, and are common to both sorts of them. As sometimes the patient through the too intense ebullition of his bloud from cordialls and hot keepeing becomes phreneticall, sometimes from the same causes, in this disease as in the Pest its self, the compages[1] of the bloud being dissolved through the violence of the inflammation purple spots appeare scatterd up and downe between the pustles and prove the certain messengers of death. This most espetially happens when the constitution of the aire is very epidemicall as to this disease. Sometimes from too hot keepeing there are decernd upon the tops of the pustles little black spots noe biger than pins heads, with dimpleings in many places, which going away through the benefit of a colder regimen, grow at length of a russet color, and after that by degrees come to that yellow which is naturall to the destinct pox. I may here adde that perhaps the flox pox its self is sometimes to be accounted but an accident of the small pox, as when the variolous matter hath been thrust out too fast in the first days of the disease by hot cordialls and immoderate warme keepeing, whereby those pox are made to flox which otherwise in their owne nature would have been destinct.

Other accidents now and then acrew from contrary causes to the before mentioned ones (viz.) from suffering the patient to incurr extreme cold, or makeing undue evacuations by bleeding purgeing etc. For hence it comes to passe that sometimes the pustles grow flat and fall on a suddain and a diarrhaea comes on that indangers the patient the variolous matter being turned inwards, and nature thereby hindered from makeing a kindely discharge of the same through the habit of the body. But these and what ever accidents else depend upon this head, occur but seldome in comparison of those caused by the other (perhaps more dangerous also though less censured) extreme.

These are the anomalous accidents belonging to the small pox when unduely handled, according to which a prognostic quite different from the before mentioned one is due to the same. It being most certaine that

[1] Compages: structure joining together (*O.E.D.*).

this disease in its self of all others the most salutary, and which if left alone would kill very few or none at all, is made through the unskilfull management of physitians led away by the notion of malignity (a word that they have read in a booke) more fatall to young men espetially than perhaps any one disease whatsoever and a just occasion of reproach upon the faculty of physick.

But now what this disease is in it[s] essence I know not nor am I able to apprehend by reason of the common and naturall defects of human understanding. But never the lesse the more strict consideration of the severall phaenomena before mentioned inclines me to beleive that it is an inflammation (though of a different species from all others) in the bloud and humors, wherein dureing the first three or four days, nature is intent upon the digestion of the inflamed particles, which afterwards being amandated to the habit of the body, she farther ripens and expells by way of severall small abscesses. Upon these premises it follows, that the curative indications are to be instituted according to those two times of natures digesting and expelling the inflamed particles, in both which alike she is neither to be precipitated nor retarded, but to be lead forwards and helped in her owne proper pace and motion. And in the meane while the inflammation is soe far to be alaid and mitigated as is consisten with the discharge of the variolous matter conformably whereunto this course I take in the cure.

As soone as I perceive the disease will prove the small pox, I forbid that patient to goe abroad, to eate flesh or drinke wine etc. Instead whereof I order him to feed on water-gruell panado etc and for his drinke to use small bear lightly warmed by puting a tost in it. I injoyne him to forbeare a hot regimen, and the use of any cordialls whatsoever in order to the strikeing them out before the fourth day which is the naturall and genuin time for eruption in regard it is most certain that the longer it be ere the small pox come out the more universall the separation of the variolous matter will be and consequently the better they will hold out and come to maturity, whereas the more early forceing them with a hot regimen and medecins precipitates the matter whilst it is yet crude and brings out a rather ripe fruit that very often comes to noe thing. Besides that this course indangers the turning them into a Flox pox. Nor is it of any moment that the patient in the meane time endures great sicknesse for want of their comeing out, for as much as it is harde to give an example of any one that hath died for want of their comeing out at first, provided they have not been hinderd from the same by a hot regimen and cordialls (for I have observed espetially upon young and sanguin persons) that the imposeing a hot regimen and the giveing cordialls in order to the bringing the small pox out, hath been soe far from answering that end, that it hath contrarywise frustrated the same. For the bloud being hereby heated, and put into a motion inconsistent with the separation of the variolous matter, noe more hath appeard then what only was sufficient, to declare it to have been the small pox untill such time as reduceing the bloud to a due and moderate temper by imposeing a contrary regimen I have given them an oportunity to come forth and thereby have retrieved the patient from ruin.

But at the end of the fourth day if then noe signes of eruption shall appeare, it may not be amisse to give a little Diascord. Pul. Gascon. or some such moderate cordiall in order to the strikeing them out they being now mature and ripe for separation.

After that time I forbeare the giveing any thing in order to that end, except a little draught of milke warmed and tincted with safron to be taken morning and evening till the pustles in the face are grown crusty which most commonly in the destinct pox is about the tenth day and in the flox pox about the twelfth. At what times instead of milke and safron I order five or six spoonfulls of old Malago tincted likewise with safron to be given thence forwards morning and evening till the patient be well. In regard that the crustynesse of the pustles at this time hindering the free evaporation of the steam proceeding from the matter now growne purulent, there is danger of the recoiling back of the said putrid steams into the mass of bloud, and consequently of the suddain death of the patient when not fortified with this or some other cordiall, and this is the true time for cordialls and not before.

But in the meane time I allow the patient to sit up some howers (according as his strength will permitt) every day dureing the whole sicknesse, provided that neither his too great soarnesse, nor the coldnesse of the season prohibit the same. And this I doe both to preserve the bloud in a due temper in this soe hot a disease as also to avoid the comeing out of sweats by which the matter is discharged that should dilute and contemporate the pox and likewise afford necessary supply for them and the swelling.

But in case, for the causes before mentioned, tis convenient to keepe the patient in bed, I suffer him however to lie with noe more clothes upon him, nor to have any other fire, then what he was accustomed to in the time of his health, nor doe I confine him to lie always in one place, but allow him the liberty of his bed, and likewise the refreshment of keepeing his armes out, provided it was his manner soe to doe when he was well.

This veryly notwithstanding the great and unreasonable prejudice entertained by the world against the same, is the true and genuin way of keepeing those that are sick of this disease, and will be found to be soe when I am in my grave. And though it will not be denied but that many recover under the use of the quite contrary regimen yet (the more is the pity considering how safe a disease this is in its owne nature) many likewise die, and more would, if they did not owe their lives either to the coldnesse of the season wherein they were attaqued or else to their haveing (though otherwise unnecessarily) been blouded. Upon which consideration if the obstinacy of friends and the patients owne feare be such as not to suffer the keepeing before mentioned, I have always thought it more secure to take bloud, which though hurtfull in its self, in that it disturbs and confounds the separation, as also subducts the pabulum that should supply both the pustles and swelling, yet doth it a little compensate for the following hot keepeing, and there by conciliate some degree of safety to this compelled practise.

Here by the way from what hath been now said, it will appeare how easy it is to solve that common doubt how it comes to passe that in the small pox soe few die amongst the common people, in comparison of the rich, which can not be thought referable to any other cause, than that they are deprived through the narrownesse of their fortunes and their rude way of liveing of the oportunitys of hurting them selves with a more precise and tender keepeing. Though yet since they likewise of late have attained to some smattering in the notion of Malignity, and to the knowledge of Methridate hartshorne posset drinke, and other cheape ways of destroying themselves, this disease hath beene more fatall then in lesse learned though wiser ages. There being not wanting some silly woman or other in every family that is skilfull enough to contribute her part in the destruction of mankinde, but only doth lesse mischief then physitians by how much she is acquainted with fewer cordialls then they. But to returne to my businesse.

It hath been above said that in the flox pox the patient if adult is troubled with a ptyalisme, if an infant with a Diarrhaea, nature haveing provided one of those two ways for the discharge of that matter which in these depressed pox could not be had equall with what is found in those other elevated ones. For this cause as I never doe endeavour the represseing of a ptyalisme in the one, soe neither doe I the stoping of a Diarrhoea in the other, both being alike absurd, and the attempting of the latter by ignorant persons led away (in this as in other diseases) with first notions and shadows of things hath occasiond the death of many a thousand poore infants. Wherefore leting their loosenesse run out I hold on my course, keepeing them sometimes up and sometimes in the cradell, ordering them if weaned the very same diet before mentioned. Nor doth the diarrhoea which sometimes comes in the begining of the small pox and attends the eruption both in growne persons and infants deserve any greater consideration, provided noe artificiall evacuation hath administered occasion thereunto. For as much as I have observed that notwithstanding such a flux may give some little chek to the more speedy comeing out of the small pox neverthelesse nature will not at length faile to turne the streame of the variolous matter to the habit of the body, noe lesse than she always doth the same matter which causeth vomiting before eruption.

As to the preserveing the face from disfigureing I finde it by sufficient experience best to use noe thing at all. In regard that all oyles, liniments etc. by their moisture doe retard the drying up of the ulcers and by this delay the sanies[1] contained in them causes the greater excavations. But there is little danger of any mischeife to the face provided the patient hath beane moderately kept and the pustles have not acquired a corrosivenesse and anger from too much heat. A certaine scurfe remaining after the dry scabs are fallen of [*sic*] which severall times peeleing off and growing again being that which in those that have been kept hot causeth the piting.

And the like may be said concerning the eys puting aside that swelling of the palpebrae which sometimes causeth blindnesse for a little time but is naturall to the disease and needeth noe other remedy saveing a little breast milk or some such slight thing now and then to be dropd in both to ease and moisten the part.

When the patient is perfectly recovered and hath eaten flesh about the space of a weeke I am carefull then to purge him and that more liberally after a flox pox or Autumnall than after Destinct or Vernall, in regard those leave the body more foule then these.

But now although this course (if carefully and wisely fitted to particular circumstances) will prevent all those unnaturall and dangerous accidents before mentioned, and render the disease most benigne and safe, yet when through the want of care and skill the said accidents have been made before I have been called, I am enforced in some particulars which I shall here recite, to alter my hand for the removeing of them.

In the first place therefor in the destinct pox if from immoderately hot keepeing and continued sweats the patients face swells not the eighth day but is lanke and lookes white in the interstitia between the pustles, in this case besides that I make all the hast I can to coole him moderately and to put him out of those sweats. I likewise order him a narcotick as about half an ounce syr. de mecon. dissolved in Cowslip water or the like, which by causeing sleepe (where the brain is not too

[1] Sanies: poison.

much heated) and thereby laying a bridle upon the ferocity of the bloud gives it and the heat an oportunity to have their recourse to the face in the way that is naturall to this disease. But if the mischeif depending upon this cause be soe far advanced that the sweat is allready vanished of its owne accord, the patient is become phreneticall and makes water in small quantitys very often, then I hold it too late (in regard that death is at the dore) for any other proceeding then takeing bloud or exposeing him to downright cold. Nor am I to be blamed for engageing upon this extreme, and scandall but those who create a necessity for the same, and indeed, if we shall but reflect upon the very frequent examples every one hath seen or heard of those who about this time of the disease have been recovered from the brink of destruction either by large haemorrhages at the nose suddainly happening or by forcibly geting loose from their nurses into the cold, what I here propose will be thought to deserve the lesse reproach. Besides that tis to be considered that in this agony the great danger of death is not conversant about the pustles strikeing in (for these, as hath been said, stand up high and red to the very last) but about the faces not swelling. Now to the bringing on of this, any thing that gives temper to the bloud, which bloudletting and cooleing can not be denied to doe, must needs conduce equally and upon the same grounds with the use of Narcoticks before mentioned. But in the meane time if this shall still seeme ridiculous, this incouragement shall any one have in laughing that every silly woman to whom appeale shall be made about the absurdity of this practise, shall justify him in his mirth and magnify his deeper still, what pitty soever his ill luck may deserve.

In the next place if in the flox pox the matter of the ptyalisme through preceding heat is soe baked up as that it is become very viscous and endangers suffocation of the patient which as hath beene said is very ordinary about the eleventh day from the invasion, in this case I am carefull above all things to order gargleing of the throat and to enjoyne with great strictness the same to be donne with a syringe very often night and day. I use either small beere with hony of roses dissolved therein or this following one: Rx. liquirit 3 drachms cortic ulmi ½ oz fol plantag. beton $\overline{\text{an}}$. ½ minim fung. sambuc N° 4 passul. enucl. N° 12 fl. samb. ros. rub. $\overline{\text{an}}$ p. i coq. s. q. aq hord. ad 12 ozs colatur dissolv. mel ros 1½ ozs syr de rub Idaeo 1 oz. m. f. gargar injiciend cum syring saepe saepius diu noctuque.[1]

[1] Rx. 3 drachms of liquorice, ½ oz. of elm bark, ½ minim each of leaves of plantain and betony. 4 elder fungi, 12 stoned grapes, 1 part each of flowers of elder and red rose. Cook in sufficient barley water, up to 12 ozs. Strain. Dissolve 1½ ozs. of rose honey, 1 oz. of syrup of blackcurrant. Mix. Make a gargle, to be injected with a syringe frequently day and night.

This frequent and assiduous use of gargleing very seldom fails of freeing the patient from the ill consequences of this accident, yet never the lesse sometimes the matter of the ptyalisme is soe impact and the dosynesse soe great, that noe gargleing whatsoever will serve the turne. This doth especially happen when the pox hath invaded like a nephriticall paroxysme or like a pleurisy, both which ways of invadeing, as hath been said, doe shew that they will prove a very high flox, and consequently that this accident will be very pressing the one alway following the degree of the other for which cause whenever the small pox invade with such pains I always take bloud before eruption to prevent the bakeing up of the ptyalisme to such a dangerous heighth as will be too hard for the patient to overcome, notwithstanding any assistance given by gargles, nor have I ever yet put the issue of preventing this mischeife upon moderate keepeing without bleeding, but judg it not absurd to have donne it in regard I am very well satisfied how great a tendency such keepeing alone hath to the preventing the same where the small pox invaded not with such pains.

As to the cure of the phrensy which in both sorts of the small pox indifferently and in any time of them is wont to be brought on by too hot keepeing and the use of cordialls, I finde the same sufficiently conquerable by altering the regimen and giveing some such narcotick as the above named. For tis carefully to be noted that every phrensy in the small pox indicates not either the bleeding or the more liberall cooleing before mentioned, but that only which happens in the destinct pox on the eighth day, and that neither (for I desire not to be mistaken) unlesse accompanied with those signes of death approaching which above I have recited.

The next of the *Accidents* mentioned as proceeding from too hot keepeing are noe lesse to be cured then avoided by the contrary keepeing, that of *Purple spots* only excepted, which declare the great malignity of the physitians practise togeather with the certainty of the patients death.

But now what ever accidents depend upon the *Recoiling* back of the variolous matter through incurring extreme cold or makeing undue evacuations, they are to be cured by the use of cordialls and a suitable regimen at least for soe long as those accidents shall last. Amongst these are chiefly to be recond the *Flating* of the pustles in the destinct pox (for as to the same in the flox pox tis but what is naturall to them) and likewise a *Diarrhaea* which for the most part attends the other but the *Diarrhaea* which either attends the eruption or is a concomitant of the flox pox in infants is not here meant. The same being as hath been said to be let alone. The cordiall which I commonly use is this: Rx. aq. paralys 2 ozs aq. theriac still 1½ drachms diascord ½ drachm elect de ov. ½ scruple syr de mecon 2 drachms.[1] M. This or the like medecin I give (and for the most part but once) not only for the removeing the above mentioned accidents but likewise when the patient complains of any *sicknesse* at his heart any time after full eruption.

This I thought fit to write both in regard that what I formerly published concerning this disease in a book of mine intituled, methodus curandi febres etc. was lesse perfect for want of those oportunitys of being thoroughly informed which since that time I have plentifully had espetially in the years 1667 and 68 in both which the small pox raged more then almost ever hath beene knowne, and likewise for that I am abundantly sensible of the great mischeifs that are dayly donne through mistakes about this disease, but espetially about its cure, wherein a great pudder is wont to be kept and the patient frightened into enduring the torment of being kept whole weeks sweltering in his bed and of being burnt up with cordialls and all to noe other effect oftentimes then the distruction of the patient or at best his cure's appearing to have been better then it was, by his haveing been made worse then he needed, both in respect of those great and dangerous accidents to which he was unnecessarily exposed dureing his sicknesse and likewise of the disfigureing impressions remaining oftentimes on his face after recovery, that otherwise would have been certainly avoided. Truly the just indignation I have both at the folly and cruelty of the received practise in this disease provokes me to appeale to the less fallible because common reason of mankinde whether the event were not to be suspected if the stoutest porter or some person under the happyest circumstances of health and vigor should be taken from his businesse and for experiment sake should be put to bed, where with the curtains close drawne and a large fire in the roome he should be kept in a sweat or (to use a softer name) in a gentle mador for some weeks, being in the meane while carefully assisted by a nurse or two who upon the least moveing from his forme or puting a finger out of bed should correct his error by heapeing on more clothes, and dureing all this time neither the use of small beer nor anything else that is accustomary or gratefull to his palat should be allowd him, but instead thereof should be constreind to drinke posset drinke or some such mixture and likewise to take cordialls of sundry kindes and in severall formes every third or fourth hour. For my owne part I should noe lesse suspect his life to be in hazard under such discipline, then his case to be very uneasy. But to be more serious I doubt not but that by such means as these, greater slaughters are committed and more havock

[1] Rx. 2 ozs. of cowslip water, 1½ drachms of Theriac, ½ drachm of diascordium, ½ scruple of electuary of egg, 2 drachms of syrup of meconium. Mix.

made of mankinde every yeare then hath been made in any age by the sword of the feircest and most bloudy tyrant that the world ever produced, and which makes it yet more sad, this distruction lights not upon any soe much as the *youth* and flourishing part of mankinde, amongst whom likewise the richest, as being the best able to be at the charges of dyeing according to art, suffer most under this calamity. But now whether I have mended the matter both in exhibiting to the world the true, if not the only history of this disease, which before lay entangled in the obscurity of notions taken up by booke men and fitted to hypotheses where with they had prepossessed themselves in their closets. Also in delivering a cure that will render this heretofore soe fatall a disease as safe as any other whatsoever, will be the question till tis tried but noe longer. And till then I doe not beg but may reasonably challeng a beleif. I know to write the history of a disease is common, but soe to doe it as not to deserve the just contempt expressed by that great Genius of Rationall nature the Lord Bacon against some undertaker of the like kinde, is somewhat more difficult. *Satis scimus haberi* (hic de morborum historia) historiam naturalem, mole amplam, varietati gratam, diligentia saepius curiosam. Attamen siquis ex eâ fabulas, et authorum citationes, et inanes controversias physiologiam denique et ornamenta eximat (quae ad convivales sermones hominumque doctorum noctes[1] potius quam ad instituendam philosophiam sint accomodata) ad nihil magni res recidet. Longe profecto abest ab eâ historia quam animo metimur.[2] Also to write the cure of a disease is not lesse ordinary but soe to doe the same as to render men as potent in actions as words will be thought a greater taske by those that shall consider that every praxis abounds with the cures of those diseases which neither the author himself nor any man since could ever cure. But let me have donne the one or the other ever soe exactly, yet neverthelesse I understand the Genius of this age, and with what it is delighted, too well to expect any other reward from men save to be reproached for my pains which would have beene bestowed more advantageously to the accomodation of my fame etc. Written by that great Genius of Physick Dr. Sydenham in July 1669.[3]

[1] "Hominumque doctorum noctes" refers to the *Noctes Atticae* of Aulus Gellius, wherein is a great mass of miscellaneous information on food, drink, travel, etc., in the form of after-dinner conversations between various savants.

[2] The following is a rough translation: "We know that this [he is talking on natural history of diseases] is considered a study of observed facts, of considerable bulk, pleasing diversity, and frequently displays the author's careful investigation. But if you subtract from it the stories, the quotations from authors, the empty disputes, and also the physiology and attempts at style (which are more suitable to dinner-table conversation or the symposia of educated men than to the scientific treatment of the subject) then this book becomes of little importance. It is certainly very far from that kind of history which I look for."

[3] From here to the end of the essay, has been roughly transcribed by Locke as a separate manuscript (B.L., MS. Locke, c. 29, f. 22).

If it be a blacke pox wherein either the pustles begin to turne black or there be blue or red or purple spots in the skin between the pustles, or it be a high flox and hot weather let them rise all day long and take noe thing but Lac Lunae. Of this black pox before he had found out the cure of it the Dr. writ as followeth.

Since my writeing the foregoing discourse of the small pox I have farther observed, that in a flox pox ordered in my way the patient begins to spit about the fifth day, his face begins to swell about the sixth, he begins to be blind about the seventh. And likewise that when the pustles are at their heigth, those on the hands and legs are large but grow lesse and lesse proportionatly as upon the limbs they are placed nearer the trunck, those on the brest back and belly being very little which also about the fourteenth day are most of them gon, when at the same time those on the hands and legs stand up high full and of a white colour. About the sixteenth or eighteenth day the patients legs begin to swell, which yet will sinke again after purgeing.[1]

I have likewise met with a sort of small pox never before by me seen. They came forth about the second day with one generall uniforme red swelling all over the face more than an erysipelas, without the least destinction of any apparent pimples at all. In the other parts of the body very red pustules arise and besides those here and there between them espetially upon the thighes severall blisters, whereof some are as big as wall nuts filled with thin water, which breaking the skin runs out and leaves the flesh under it mortified. In the progresse of the disease a white shineing skin comes on upon the red swelling in large patches in severall parts of the face never the lesse remaining still red. This white skin in a little while spews up a glary crusty matter which is not as in the other sorts of small pox either yellow or russet but of a deepe red colour till it come at last to a perfect black. I have seen triall both of hot and cold keeping in this species but neither of them have succeeded, though I finde by how much the colder they are kept by soe much are the securer from mortifications and I am apt to beleive that bleeding joyned with moderate keepeing would doe well. 62.

[1] From here to the end of the essay has been crossed out in the original.

A DYSENTERY[1]

The year *1669* hath produced the same feaver with those of the years '67 and '68 and the cure which I adapted thereunto hath beene the same which before I mentioned to be imployed about the cureing of those. But about August ⟨the foregoeing part of the somer haveing proved very hot and dry and the bloud and humors there by havening arrived to a great adustion and sharpnesse⟩ this yeare cholera morbus gripeing in the bowells without stooles and dysenterys became very epidemicall, ⟨of which there had scarce been any sprinkleings for about 10 years befor at least in this place.⟩

The Cholera morbus was by me cured according to the method I have published.

The gripeing of the bowells I cured after the same manner as I did the Dysentery of which I shall here treat.

I observe this disease come on for the most part about the begining of Autumn. It is sometimes accompanied with a feaver and sometimes without but always with great torment in the bowells upon goeing to stoole with frequent dejections and these for the most part not stercorous but mucous with which are mixt streaks of bloud in the begining, but in the farther progresse of the disease bloud in larger quantitys and unmixed often is evacuated, ⟨to the great hazard of the patients life if not the certainty of the loss of the same, this large bleeding espetially if unmixed with mucous matter being an argument of the great corrosion of some of the vessells of the intestines.⟩ Upon the continuance of this disease the intestines seeme to be affected successively downwards until the whole mischeife be terminated upon the rectum in a tenesmus wherein contrary wise then dureing the dysentery the stooles which prove stercorous cause the greatest pains in the bowells, those faeces grateing upon the yet tender guts in their passage downwards, and the mucuous stooles only troubleing the lower gut, whilst they are excreting and provokeing frequently to stoole. This disease provided it be not quickly cured ⟨is not only full of torment but likewise very dangerous to the patient whose smaller stock of vitall heate and spirits will be carried of with his frequent dejections before the peccant matter in his bloud can be excretd and coldnesse of hands and feet comeing on he will be in danger of dyeing within the period of acute diseases as

[1] B.L., MS. Locke, c. 29, ff. 19–20 (1670).

likewise that the bowells by the great inflammation from the afflux of the morbific matter to the pained part are often irrecoverably gangrend besides that as hath been observd often times through that great corrosion of the vessels, the long bearing downe of sharp humours upon them whereby a great evacuation of sincere bloud is caused, as considerable a danger is caused.> It is for the most part mortall to old persons, lesse fatall though very dangerous to youth but benigne enough to infants, who if let alone and not tamperd with may have it for some months without any prejudice of their lives. The Irish dysentery is not here meant with the nature and manner of which I am unacquaintd but that which happens in our owne country. <I judged that the curative indication was altogether to be directed to the diluteing and contemporateing the sharp humours that were excreted from the mass into the bowells, as likewise to diluteing and contemporateing the bloud its self the source of this mischeife.>

This therefor is the way of cure. If the patients be in his flourishing age and hath a feaver take bloud from his arme an hower or 2 after which take the following course. Take 4 gallons of whey, let the patient drinke thereof in soe great a quantity as by overchargeing his stomach to vomit up what he hath drunke and let him doe the same successive till he hath dranke about 3 gallons and let the rest be put up by way of clyster without the addition of sugar or anything else only a little luke warme, at 6 or 7 times one after another, putting up a fresh one as soone as he hath renderd the former. The clysters may be given between while as he is vomiting; his gripes will cease and his bloudy stooles likewise after the 4th clyster. As soone as the whey is all out of his body, and he hath gonne through this course which is donne in 3 or 4 howers if closely followed let him goe to bed and in a little time he will of his owne accord fall into a gentle breathing in which he must be kept 24 howers at least drinking noething in the meantime but raw milke a little warmed and for 3 or 4 days likewise after he riseth he must take noe thing else either for meat or drinke. If from riseing too soone or in intermitting his milke diet he relaps he must take the same course again and be wiser next time. <This way of cure will not be thought less expeditious and certain then courses usually praescribed are both tedious and dangerous, when the world valuing learning for that only therein which is necessary for the good of human life shall think as well of him that taught to cure disease as those that taught to discourse learnedly about them—et extinctus amabitur idem.> When there is noe feaver accompanying this disease it will not be necessary to take bloud before the use of the whey, espetially in ancient people, whereas if there be a feaver bloudletting is soe altogeather requisite that without it the drinking of whey and all the following meanes would be wholy ineffectuall.

This course always succeeded (provided the disease was not come to a tenesmus) dureing the heat of the yeare, but when the weather came to be cold this administration could not be used without more inconvenience though it brought less certaine advantage to the patient and I was therefor fain to substitute this other following method of cureing. I gave the patient a moderat astringent purge two mornings following, and the night after each purge a gentle narcotick. E.G. Rx Rhabarb incis. 2 drachms myrobal citrin 2 scruples santal citrin 1 scruple coq. s. q. aq. colatur iii ozs dissolv. syr. ros. solut. 1 oz rhabar. pulv. ½ drachm m. f. potio. cap. mane.

Rx Aq. Plantag. i oz. aq. cinam. fort. gr. x Laud Helm. gr. xiiii syr. de mecon. 2 drachms m. cap. eadem nocte.[1]

If the patient be an infant that hath this disease let him be kept to raw milke only and let noe thing else be donne till he be well.

But if the disease be turned into a Tenesmus the patient will be inforced to submitt unto the disease untill by the use of a nourishing diet and now and then some cordialls likewise his strength come on, proportionally to the attainment whereof this symptom will vanish of its owne accord.

Upon the invasion of winter and very hard weather the cholera morbus gripeing of the guts and dysentery above mentioned totaly ceased and instead of them the small pox (which in the sommer of this yeare as it had donne in the same season of the preceding yeare was almost gon) returned again and became more rife in which posture it continues at the writing hereof viz the beginning of the yeare 1670.

Ex attenta et faelice observatione,

Tho Sydenham.

[1] Rx. 2 drachms of sliced rhubarb, 2 scruples of lemon myrobalans, 1 scruple of lemon sandal. Cook in sufficient water. Strain. In 3 ozs. dissolve 1 oz. of dissolved rose syrup and ½ drachm of powdered rhubarb. Mix. Make a potion. Take in the morning.

Rx. 1 oz. of Plantain water, 10 grains of strong cinnamon water, 14 grains of Helmont's Laudanum, 2 drachms of syrup of meconium. Mix. Take the same night.

FEBRES INTERCURRENTES[1]

[Mend this to be put in just before the small pox][2]

These severall fevers ariseing (as neare as I can judge by contemplating the phaenomena incident both to the diseases and their cure) from an inflammation of the blood peculiar and proper to each of them I lay the foundation of curing them in cooleing and contemperating, adapting nevertheless such different methods of discharging their respective morbific matters, as is suitable to the genius of each disease, and unto which I find by constant experience it doth most naturally and kindly yield. And indeed in all fevers the great knack of curing well and certainly, is to be assured what discharge is due to the febrile matter as whether the same be to be done by way of bleeding, sweating, purging etc. Which consideration (as to the stationary fevers at least) will enable likewise to know the kind.

[1] B.L., MS. Locke, c. 29, f. 21.

[2] This manuscript was followed by one on smallpox (B.L., MS. Locke, c. 29, f. 22). It has not been included here as the same observations were incorporated in the long essay on smallpox printed earlier.

PLEURISIE[1]

Pleuritic feaver without pain

This disease then which scarce any is more common invades at any time of the yeare but espetially at that season which is between spring and summer, the bloud at that time from the approach of the sun being disposd to an effavescency and disorderly commotion, it assaults for the most part persons of a sanguin and flourishing temperament. It usually begins with a rigor and horror which is succeeded with a heate inquietude and thirst and other common symptoms attending fevers. After some few howers, though sometimes after a longer space, the patient is taken with a violent pain and stitch shooting in one of his sides about the ribs which shoots up sometimes towards his shoulder and sometimes out towards the back boan or contrary wise towards the fore part of his breast. He is often provoked to cough which proves very painfull to him from the straining thereby of the inflamed parts in soe much that he catches in his breath and endeavours to suppresse the cough upon every first motion of the same.

<He spits up after every coughing a matter which in the begining of the disease is very little in quantity, thin and mixed with streaks of bloud, but in the progress thereof is for the most part more plentiful thick and better concocted but mixed allso with bloud.>

<Sometimes when the disease is very violent and bloud hath not been taken the patient is not able to cough at all but takeing his breath with great difficulty he is as it were almost strangled, by the greatness of the inflammation which without intollerable pain allows not soe free an expansion of his breast as is requisite to sufficient breathing.> The feaver all this while is concurreing and receaves increase also from the symptoms which its self produced but the same fever togeather with the accidents of a cough, spitting of bloud pain etc proportionably lessen as the matter of the pleurisy proceeds to a full and free expectoration. But the pleuriticall matter doth not always in the progress of the disease receive this concoction fit for expectoration for it often happens that the matter which is brought up remains still little in quantity and thin as in the begining, and the feaver consequently with all the other symptoms still hold up in their greatest vigor till the patient dyes. [Dureing this time the patient is sometimes bound in his body and at other times again falls into a diarrhoea where in the dejections are both

[1] B.L., MS. Locke, c. 29, ff. 23–4.

frequent and very liquid.] Sometimes where the inflammation hath been great and seasonable bleeding neglected in the begining, it quickly grows to an impostumation, and the matter thereof is emptied out into the cavity of the thorax, in which respect although there be an abatement if not a totall cessation of the primary feaver nevertheless an hectick comes on and the patient dyes tabid.[1]

This disease in it owne nature is more dangerous than most. But if duely managed admits of cure, and with as much certainty as is suitable to the undertaking of humane endeavours in saving of mens lives, and as much as most other diseases are capable of.

Upon the consideration of the severall phaenomena of this disease I can judge it noe other thing, but fever from a peculiar inflammation of the bloud wherein nature endeavours to discharge the peccant matter upon the pleura and sometimes upon the lungs, also when it constitutes a peripneumonia: which latter I suppose differs from the former only according to the more intense degree and farther extent of one and the same cause.

That therefore which I propose to my self in the cureing of this disease is to extinguish the inflammation of the bloud and to draw back by suitable evacuations the inflamed particles that are excreted upon the membran which invests the ribs and thereby causes inflammation of those parts.

Wherefore laying the chiefest stress on bleeding as soon as I am cald I order 10 or 12 ozs. of bloud to be taken from the arme of the affected side. <The bloud at least after the first takeing, when it is cold looks on the top as if it were coverd over with melted and congealed tallow, sometimes of a considerable thickness, which being separated from the rest of the bloud proves to be a huge fibrous skin which probably is noething else but the fibrous parts of the bloud, which praecipitation having stript them of their ordinary and naturall redness doe by the coldnesse of the air unite and grow to geather into this whiteish membrane.>

<Then I order him the following potion: Rx. aq. papav. rhad. etc capiat M.[2] and likewise to take frequently pectorall medecins as Rx. decoct. pectoral 1½ lbs. syr. viol. ol. capill. veneris ān 1½ ozs. m. f. apoz. de quo capiat ½ lb. ter in die. Rx. ol. amyg. d. 2 ozs. syr viol. ol. capil veneris ān 2 ozs. sacchar cand. ½ drachm f. s. q. ecleg. de quo lambat. saepius in die[3] [oyle of sweet almonds alone often taken or linseed oyl

[1] i.e. by wasting.

[2] Rx. water of red poppy, etc. Take in the morning.

[3] Rx. 1½ pints of pectoral decoction, 1½ ozs. each of oil of violet and maidenhair. Mix. Make an apozem, of which take ½ pint thrice a day. Rx. 2 ozs. oil of sweet almonds, 2 ozs. each of syrup of violets and oil of maidenhair, ½ drachm of candied sugar. Make an eclegma which he is to sip several times a day.

new drawne ad 2 ozs. doth well]; for his ordinary food I forbid the use of all flesh even the thinest broth and enjoyn him to feed on barely broth watergruell panado etc; for his drink I order him the following ptysan: Rx. hord. mund. 1 oz. coq. aq. font. s. q. ad 2 lbs. sub finem add. liquirit $\frac{1}{2}$ oz. sem anis. 2 scruples colatur. sit pro potu ordinario.>[1] [mend to continue the use of these remedys till cured.] <I likewise order the following oyntment: Rx. ol. lil. amyg. d. et ung. dialth. $\overline{an}$ 1 oz. m. f. lin. quo. inung. latus dolens Mane superponendo fol. brasicae.>[2]

The same day if the pain be exceeding violent or the next however, I order bloud to be taken again in the same quantity and soe the 2 next days following and thus I repeat bloudleting 4 days, if the patient be not well sooner, successively where the pain and other symptoms continue to be very presseing, but when the danger and fierceness of the disease will allow slower proceeding or the weaknesse of the patient not safely beare soe quick a repitition of leting bloud I doe after the second time interpose one or 2 days between each venesection where in I am regulated by the contraindications of the violence of the disease on one side and the weaknesse of the patient on the other put in the ballance one with the other, and though I seldom in cureing of diseases tie my self to the takeing a precise quantity of bloud, yet I have rarely found that a confirmed pleurysy in an adult person would be cured with a lesse expence then 42 ounces though yet in children once bleeding hath for the most part proved sufficient. Nor doth the loosenesse which will ever now and then breake out during the days of bleeding at all hinder me from proceeding in the repitition of drawing bloud, which in its self will stop in this method without the use of any astringent medecin whatsoever. In the days where in noe bloud is taken I praescribe a gentle clyster of milke and sugar or the like. Dureing the whole diseas I require the patient not to keep himself to [*sic*] hot and to rise some howers every day according as his strength will beare, which is of soe great moment in the cure of this disease that if the patient be kept constantly soakeing in his bed, all this great evacuation of bloud and other remedys how cooling soever will sometimes signifie but little for takeing down the foremencond symptoms.

Upon the last bleeding (if not sooner) all the symptoms will abate and the patient, who for some days longer is to abstaine from all manner of strong liquors and gross diet will quickly recover his former

[1] Rx. 1 oz. cleaned barley. Cook in sufficient spring water (up to 2 pints). At the end add $\frac{1}{2}$ oz. of liquorice and 2 scruples of aniseed. Strain. Use as his ordinary drink.

[2] Rx. 1 oz. each of oil of lilies, oil of sweet almonds, and marshmallow ointment. Mix. Make a liniment for anointing the painful side in the morning, placing on top a cabbage leaf.

strength about which time it may be convenient for him to take some lenient purge.

Now if it shall be thought that in this way of cure sufficient notice is not taken of expectoration, nor rules set downe about ordering the same in its severall seasons, it is not that I have not carefully thought thereof, but that I have always judgd that way of discharge to be too dangerous an issue upon which to put the cure, for besides the tedium thereof there is likewise great hazard in manageing this way of natures discharging the morbific matter it often happening that whilst some part is concocted and perhaps discharged likewise by expectoration other parts thereof remain crude and soe successively not withstanding the use of the best ripening and expectorating medicins whatsoever. The patient sometimes expectorates well and at other times not at all incurring in the meane time the great danger that is justly pronouncd upon a pleuritis sicca [and soe my patient may live or dye according as I am able to command expectoration]. Whereas in this way of discharge by downright bloud letting I have the morbifick matter at my command and doe make the orifice made by the lancet to serve in stead of the trachea and I dare also confidently affirm that this disease which managed according to those precepts here rejected by me is one of the great windeing sheets of nature, is by this other way here proposd is as certainly and safely cured (not to mention the speed thereof) as any disease whatsoever. Nor have I ever known any bad effects follow upon the loosing such seemingly great quantitys of bloud.

Q. What is to be don if cald after expectoration is upon the wholl . . .

Q. Empyema.

FEBRES INTERMITTENTES[1]

It hath been said in the begining of my observations touching continued fevers that there was great difference between them in respect of the different constitutions of severall yeares, but that there was noe such difference to be discerned amongst them as to the different seasons of the same yeare. Contrary to which it comes here to be observed that intermitting fevers are the same in all yeares whatsoever. Though perhaps as the constitution of the yeare prove more or less epidemicall for this or that intermittent, the same like wise may prove more or less diuturnall accompanied also with more dangerous or else more favourable symptoms, all the difference otherwise that is to be discerned between them is cheifly in respect of the two most eminent seasons of the same yeare, some accordingly being proper to one time of the yeare, and others to an other. And though other seasons of the yeare besides those two may sometimes produce them, yet never the lesse they belong properly to the nearest of the fore mentioned seasons to the time wherein they happen for sometimes there may be so great an apparatus in the temper of the aire to some or other of these intermittents that either of them may begin to appear a good while before the season to which it respectively belongs, an instance of which was in the yeare 1661 wherein quartans and autumnall tertians that then exceedingly reigned appeared first about midsomer. But sometimes on the other hand there is so little suitableness in the air to such agues that they, from some provision laid up in this or that man's body, may happen a good while after either of those two seasons. But generally, and for the most part, February and August are the terms respectively belonging to spring or fall agues: those of the spring are quotidians and tertians, those of the fall quotidian, tertian, and quartans, the latter of which is as it were the true and genuin ofspring of this season. Now although the quotidians and tertians of one season may not seem to differ from the same of the other in regard that their tipe is the same as like wise their manner of invadeing with a rigor and horror succeeded with heat and that with sweat, yet never the less, it will appeare from the vehemency of their symptoms, suddain dejection of strength, sicknesse even between the fits, the length of their duration, their natural tendency to quite different diseases, and other phaenomena that they essentially differ.

[1] B.L., MS. Locke, c. 29, ff. 25–8.

All of them begin with a rigor and horror which is succeeded by heat and that afterwards by a sweat. Dureing the cold and the hot fit the patient is troubled for the most part with reaching to vomit and great sicknesse with thirst and a dry tongue etc. which symptoms goe off proportionably to the comeing on of the sweat this seemeing to be the solution of the fit. The patient remains well till the period wherein the fit comes about. <Which in a quotidian is once in about twenty four hours in a tertian every other day in a quartan every third day reconing from the beginning of one fit to the begining of the next. Though yet the two later frequently double soe that the tertian comes every day and the quartan two days togeather the third being free and some times thrice in three days when it proves a treble quartan the disease being denominatd from the type it tooke when it first invaded which doubling proceeds sometimes from the excesse of the aguish matter, and the over activity there of and in that case the bastard fit anticipates and sometimes from the want of strength when the patient hath been too much weakened and the vigor of his fit abated by too much cooleing or too large evacuations, and in this case the adventitious fit succeeds the true one and in both is the lesser of the two. In the former case the turgescens of the matter attends not the too slow returne of the usuall period and therefor spends its self in some degree before hand, in the later the bloud not being strong enough to carry of all the febrile matter at one fit, is faine to substitute an other soon after to rid its self of the remainder upon which two contrary causes perhaps also may depend the anticipation or postponing of the fit in the ordinary course of a regular ague which in these agues doth often happen and they run round the whole 24 howers anticipating or postponing as hath been said. And tis worthy the takeing notice of when at any time those agues especially autumnall ones come in in shoales, their fits upon severall persons usually agree in the same day and hower of the day and soe keepe pace togeather both in their anticipation and postponeing unlesse that regular order be disturbed by a different management which may delay or hasten the fit.> This also is observable that often times in the begining of agues espetially epidemicall ones of the fall tis very hard to discerne their tipe for the first days where in they attaque for as much as they begin with a continued fever and tis not easy for a good while without great care to observe any thing more than a remission which never the less by degrees falls into an intermission and under a type proper to the season, and fits.

Spring agues I have observd to be for the most part not long lasting but to be constantly salutary how old or weake soever the patient be he cannot be killed by any tampering how contrary soever that is competent to a physitian that doth but meane well. Though yet I have knowne that in tertians at this season the ague through bleeding purgeing and other ill managment hath run out to a long diuturnity lasting even to ⟨the time that autumnall agues usually come in which season being so quite contrary to the genius and nature of this disease doth not faile to give a finall dismission unto it⟩ and the patient in the meane time by the often doubling of his fits as well as their continuance hath been reduced to extreme weaknesse threatning death which however I have never yet observed to happen, nor after the totall cessation of the disease have I at least taken notice that any of those ill accidents of a fatall soare throat ague cake[1] hydropicall swellings etc. which follow long autumnall agues, have succeeded those. ⟨But autumnall agues are far otherwise for first for the tertian though when it is not very Epidemicall and ceises likewise bodys that are healthy and flourishing it may goe of as speedily and accompanied with as few ill accidents as tertians happening in the other season yet in years wherein it is epidemicall and in persons who are of declining years and an ill habit of body it often proves very dangerous and also frequently runs out sometimes two sometimes three months if not to the next spring. And secondly as to quartans they are yet more dangerous and of far longer continuance allso than those last mentiond, for when they ceise upon old bodys they often kill in some one or other of the first fits, the patient in such case dyeing for the most part in the cold fit, and admitting the patient not to be soe old however if he be past his prime though he run not the same hazard of dyeing in the beginning yet it will hang upon him at leaste till the return of the same season wherein he was first taken, and sometimes linger till it brings him languishing to his grave. The quartan in the mean time often varying its tipe and produceing likewise accidents of sundrey kindes as jaundice dropsies. But young persons beare this disease well enough which they shake of about the winter solstice, though usually it hold them to the vernall equinox following, and it hath been often matter of great astonishment to me how well even the tenderest infants have borne this disease for six months togeather. Here it is to be rememberd that of what age or constitution soever the patient be that is taken with a quartan if at any time of his life though never soe long before he have been troubld with the same disease it will not upon the second returne prove very lasting but quickly goe off of its owne accord.

Now the accidents which both attend this disease in its declination and likewise follow it are the same which attend and follow the other autumnall ague when it proves very diuturnall for in both often the

[1] Ague Cake—disease of spleen or liver caused by the ague.

patient becomes very scorbuticall, hath a hard belly especially towards the region of the spleen, and fall into the jaundice, sometimes is troubled with swellings which in children is of the belly, in ancient men is of the legs first, and afterwards of the belly likewise when it comes to a dropsie, and tis observable that those long autumnall agues seldom forsake children till they have brought on the forementiond swelling and hardnesse of their belly especially about the region of the spleen, and then the ague decays proportionably as this swelling comes on, which brings with it one of the certainest prognostiques of the departure of the ague in a little time after. The same holds in these swellings which are observed to ceise on the legs of growne people.>

As to the cure of Vernall agues I am very positive in my opinion grounded upon sufficient experience that it is the best way to let them alone enjoyning neither medecins diet nor regimen, but however if this satisfies not my patient when I have my conscience in telling him what I think is best, but he importunes a cure then <if it be a quotidian I order the patient to carry on the sweat which happens in the end of the fit with marigold posset drinke and perhaps also with some slight diaphoretique medecin soe much and soe long as the patients strength will permitt, which course often cures in this ague but seldome doth it in a tertian of the same season and never in a tertian or quartan of the fall, if it be a tertian> I attempt the cure one of these ways: Either to give a vomit of infusion of Crocus in such a time that it may have donne working soe timely that there may be roome to give a moderate quantity of syr. de meconium in a convenient vehicle an hower or two befor the fit comes on. Or by ordering a Clyster of milk and sugar to be injected the intermitting days and injoyning a precise fasting twenty four howers before their fit, continueing it untill the fit be over and if the patient be not able to fast soe long I only allow him a very small quantity of barely broth and a little small beer in the succeeding hot fit prescribing in the meane time the use of this following cordiall Rx. aq. card. ben. bujal. a̅n̅ 4 ozs. aq. scordii compos syr. de limon et caryophyl a̅n̅ 1 oz. m. f. juleb de quo cap. coch. 6 vel 8 saepe saepius per decursum diei jejunii.[1] Those who are bleeded for Vernall agues and are not by it immediately cured are soe far from receiving benefit there by that this losse of bloud setles the disease faster and makes it run out to the longest period of vernall agues.

In the management of Autumnall agues I have always observed it to be very dangerous to attempt their cure by [cathartiques other than that which shall be hereafter mentioned but] espetially that of takeing of

[1] Rx. 4 ozs. each of water of carduus benedictus and bugle, 1 oz. each of water of water-germander, syrup of lemons and cloves. Mix. Make a juleb. Take 6 or 8 spoonfuls quite frequently on the day of fasting.

bloud, for in tertians espetially where the constitution is very epidemicall if the cure hath been taken that way and the cure yet missed thay have in bodys, though never soe young and well habitid, run out to a great diuturnity. But in ancient persons the diuturnity hath likewise been followed with the death of the patient which very often the fatall soar throat mentiond in the end of my observations of continued feavers hath ushered in; besides that the said bleeding hath hastened those other accidents which I have said doe accompany autumnall agues in their declination or follow them. And in quartans bleeding is soe prejudiciall that in young men who otherwise would of course have parted with their agues in six months it fixes them for a twelve month. And declining persons who otherwise might have lost them in a twelve month doe now incur the danger of keepeing them longer even than that and at length of sinking under them.

As to Autumnall quotidians I have not observed what is sufficient to enable me to speake much though I have noe great reason to doubt but that they may be cured with these next to be mentioned. To remove Autumnall tertians this I doe: the patient being laid warme and well coverd in his bed I raise a sweat with sage posset drinke about four howers before the [comeing on the fit and as soone as he is got into a sweat I order him to take pil. coch. maj. 2 scruples dissolved in 1 oz. seq. juleb. Rx. vin. adust. 8 ozs. theriac androm 3 ozs. cochinel 3 ozs. croc. Angl. 1 drachm m. stent simul pro usu.[1] When he has taken this let him carefully continue *the sweat for some howers after the time of his fit be over carefully fenceing against that interruption of his sweat which may be given him by some stooles that the medecin may occasion. If it be a double tertian which has changed its type by evacuating or any other weakening of the patient sweat is after the same manner to be raised and at the same distance of time before the true fit either with the before mentiond medecin leaveing out the pil. coch. [it being neither safe nor effectuall to the cure to give purgeing medecins where the patient is all ready weakned by them and the doubleing of the ague brought on thereby]*[2] or some other that is very high and operative to the intention of sweating which may likewise be repeated the next true fit. And if a very high debilitation of strength be upon the patient togeather with this doubleing then I prescrib this following electury: Rx. cons. fl. borag. bugloss anthos. ān 1 oz. cortic. citri condit. zz. condit. nucis mosc. condit et theriac. Androm. ān ½ oz. confect. alker. 3 ozs. m. f. opiat de qua cap. ad magnitudinem avellanae mane superbibendo coch. 6 vel 8 seq. juleb.

[1] Rx. 8 ozs. of burnt wine, 3 ozs. of theriac of Andromachus, 3 ozs. of cochineal, 1 drachm of English saffron. Mix. Let them stand before use.

[2] The passage between the two asterisks has been repeated in MS.

Rx. aq. theriac 2 ozs. syr. caryophil. 1 oz.[1] or instead thereof some plaine plague water sweetend with sugar prohibiting in the meane time the use of clysters. I keep the patient to the use of chicken broath, watergruell etc.

But now as to the cure of quartans it is not yet my happynesse to be able to master the same and by what I yet know I judge it the best course to let them alone both in respect of regimen and medecins save that I observe it doth greatly import the patient to indulge to the moderate use of such strong liquors as are agreeable to his palat amongst which wormwood wine or wormwood bere are of great use in that they preserve the tone of his parts and inable him for the undergoing this soe highly diuturnall a disease. As also that I observe that the patients removeing himself into an other aire and that if may into a more southerne just about that time when the ague was first capable of leaveing him which is six months after his first being taken is of great use to the shortening of the disease. But to remove sooner is not beneficiall how hot soever the climat is to which the patient goes.

Q What disease spring agues have a tendency too.

Q Sweat whether to be promoted and the end of the fit in quartans and other agues.

When the patient is quite freed from either of these intermitting fevers great care is to be taken about duely purgeing him for tis incredible what a trayne of soare distempers follow the omission thereof. After agues espetially if they have beene very diuturnall how wanting soever physitians have been in cautioning the same, for when soever I have observed any one long labouring under one of these agues, espetially if he hath been ancient or the ague a quartan and hath omitted purgeing upon the going off of his ague, I could certainly fore tell that he would not long after be taken with some dangerous distemper of which beleaving [him]self perfectly recovered he had not yet the least apprehension. But in the meane time great caution must be used that the patient be not purged before his ague be perfectly gon for although some portion of the dregs of the disease thrown off upon the natural parts may hereby seem to be evacuated never the lesse from the ague that will be here by recald new matter will suddainly be heaped up whereby not only the purgation will be renderd ineffectuall but the disease likewise will be made more lasting. [Frequent instances of the truth of this we may every day observe in those who in the

[1] Rx. 1 oz. each of conserve of the flowers of borage, bugloss, and anthos, ½ oz. each of cooked lemon peel, cooked ginger, cooked nutmeg, and theriac of Andromachus, 3 ozs. of confection of Alkermes. Mix. Make an opiate. Take a piece the size of a filbert in the morning, washing it down with 6 or 8 spoonfuls of this juleb. Rx. 2 ozs. of theriac water and 1 oz. of syrup of cloves.

declining of the ague in complyance with the phisitians notions of opening obstructions and carrying off the stubborne melancholy humour the supposd cause of this disease are disciplind with reiteratd purges by which what ever humors may be loosend and carried of from the body tis certain the ague is soe much the more fixed that it continues longer than otherwise it would have done.] For which reasons I abstain from purgeing the patient, till not only the sensible paroxysms are quite vanished, but even till all alteriety in those days where in the fit should come is likewise gon and for a month longer, at what time I praescribe my common lenient potion and order the same once a weeke for two or three months following not failing to give some quieting medecin in the close of its workeing each time to prevent the returne of the fit which might be other wise occasiond by the tumult and disorder that is raised by the purgeing, even by the gentlest purging medecins.

Now as to the cure of the accidents which either attend these agues in their declination or follow them when gon, some thing being to be said. In the first place little is to be donne towards the removeing of them whilst the ague remains for by those purgeing remedys by which a dropsie hardnesse of the belly etc. might otherwise be cured the ague as hath been said will take deeper rooting and consequently the accident depending there upon not admit of cure excepting that I have observed that in the swelling of the legs continuing on in the declination of agues the drinking every morning half a pint of Rhenish wine wherein hath been infused a quantity of horse radish root and worm-wood doth not only not interfere with the ague but also cures that symptom. Nor doth the administring anti-scorbutic remedys provided that therewith purgatives be not mixed doe more harme. But as to the accidents which follow they are most of them easily removed with opening and cathartic medicins provided the ague be quite gon in soe much that even dropsies that have supervend these agues and would seeme to threaten great danger doe very easily yield unto the use of them. Nor are infants with more difficulty to be cured who often times after these autumnall intermittents become rickity haveing swollen and hard bellys, being hecticall, troubled with a cough, and other symptoms of being in a consumption with whom this course I take, which too I have seldom known to faile, the cureing of the rickets. I give of my common lenient potion coch 1 or 2 more or less according to the childs age for nine mornings intermitting now and then a day as I see occasion soe ordering the dose of my purge that it may give as often as it is taken about five or six stooles. This purgeing course being ended I anoint the childs belly all over for severall days to geather with some aperient oyntment. This following I often use: Rx. ol. lil. tamar, an̄ 2 ozs. succ. rad. brion. et apii an̄ 1 oz. bull. ad succor. consumptionem addend. ung. de alth. et butyr. insuls. an̄ 1 oz. gum. ammon. in aceto solut. ½ oz. cer. fl. q. s. m. f. linim.[1]

Here I thought fit to note that I have observed this accident of a hard belly which I looke upon to be one of the surest notes of the Rickets, either approaching or in being, never comes on after any other feavers of which I have treated saving amongst the continued fevers after the depuratory and amongst the intermitting after the autumnall, the inflation of the belly which often comes after other feavers having such an hardnesse as usually accompanies tension; where as the former swollen bellys feele hard from something lying within stuffeing and hardening the parts.

Another accident there is which sometimes succeeds those intermittents, but is so far from yeilding to purging and evacuations espetially bloud letting that it is highly inraged by the use of them, and that is a certain kinde of maddnesse agreeing in all the symptoms with the mania described by physitians but wholy different in its cure, which has hitherto in the ordinary practise beene so little adapted to this species, where of noe notice is taken as differing in any respect from the other, that it is wholy prejudiciall to it, and whereas other maddnesse is usually favoured by very large evacuations both of bloud and purgeing, this sort will not beare the least of either of them, but even when it is in a very faire way of recovery be brought quite back again by one simple clyster of milke and sugar. [And if the cure of it be attempted by repeated purgeing and bleeding such evacuations will master the raveing feircenesse of the disease but with all will be sure to bring the patient to a miserable fatuity.] Which will not seeme strange to any who but considers that end that proceeds from too high and vigorous a constitution of bloud, the other from the weakenesse and as it were vapidness of the same whereby spirits are made too disproportional to the animal functions. Thus I cure it. I order the patient to take thrice every day one high cordialls of some two others sorts and in larg quantitys, as venice treacle electuary de ovo, pulv. comitiss.[2] Sr W. Roughley[3] etc. in aq. opid Theriacal etc. V.g. Rx. Ther. Andr. 2 ozs. elect de ovo ½ oz. pulv. e chel. cancr. compos. rad. centr. cerv: cochinel. an̄ 1 drachm croci veri 2 scruples cum. s. q. syr.

[1] Rx. 2 ozs. each of oil of lilies and tamarinds, 1 oz. each of juice of radish, bryony, and parsley. Boil till the juices are consumed, adding 1 oz. each of unguent of marshmallow and unsalted butter, ½ oz. of gum ammoniac dissolved in vinegar, and sufficient yellow wax. Mix. Make a liniment.

[2] Pulvis Cometissae is one of the oldest formulae for the administration of Peruvian Bark (see *Works*, vol. 1, p. cii).

[3] Sir Walter Raleigh's powder or confectio aromatica.

e cortic citr. f. elect. de q. capiat ad magnitudinem nuc. moscat. ter in die horis medicinalibus superbibendo 2 ozs. sequentis juleb. Rx. aq. scord. compos. 6 ozs. therical stillat an̄ 4 ozs. aq. imperial 2 ozs. confect alker. 2 drachms syr. caryophy. 1 oz.[1] cordials also in sundry other formes may be given. The patient in the mean time is to be kept to a moderat, but yet a restorative diet, and for his drinke to use the strongest sort of liquors and to keepe within dores and much in bed likewise. The patient will be apt under this management to be bound from which as likewise from the use of these hot remedys one would feare a feaver but there is noe danger thereof, his spirits haveing beene soe much exhausted by the past feaver. The patient after some weeks will begin to amend at what time the cordialls may now and then be omitted for some days but the restorative diet still continued and soe to return to agen, and persist in, the use thereof till the cure be perfected. This how contemptible soever it may seeme will cure this sort of madnesse. Though this, nor anything else, will the madness of those men who raving upon remote philosophicall notions contemp the easier and plainer ways of doeing good to his neigbour.

[1] . . . venice treacle, electuary of egg, Countess's powder and Sir W. Raleigh's powder in water of theriac, etc. E.g. Rx. 2 ozs. of theriac of Andromachus, ½ oz. of electuary of egg, 1 drachm each of powdered crab's claws, compound of stag's horn and cochineal, 2 scruples of true saffron, with sufficient syrup of lemon rind. Make an electuary. Take some the size of a nutmeg thrice a day at the usual times for medicine, washing it down with this juleb. Rx. 6 ozs. of water of water-germander, 4 ozs. of theriac, 2 ozs. of imperial water, 2 drachms of confection of Alkermes, 1 oz. of syrup of cloves.

OF THE FOUR CONSTITUTIONS[1]

From the proportion of the vent to the heat doe arise all the internell causes of the 4 constitutions. That which is vented slowest of all is melancholy. The next cholerick, the next sanguin. That which vents fastest of all is Phlegmaticke by drawing the liquor into the veins before it is concocted I meane by the proportion a weake and slow heat ought to have a weake and slow vent and a strong and quicke heat ought to have a strong and quicke vent. And the same moreover for time of venting in our body which hath a strong heat causes melancholy or choller the which in another body which hath a weaker heat causeth only sanguine or Phlegme in reference to the degree of heat which concocts as the same aliment may in the space of 3 dayes be incinerated to melancholy or adjusted to choller by a strong and violent heat which by a temperatt heat is only concocted to sanguine and by a weake hardly arrives to phlegme in that space.

The stronger and quicker the vent to a weake and slow heat the more Phlegmaticke and sanguine is the constitution.

The more slow and weake the vent is to a strong and quicke heat the more melancholy is the constitution.

Children having a quick vent to a weake heat are therefore Phlegmaticke.

Young men having a quick vent to a strong heat are therefore sanguine so that in these the vent and heat are proportionable. Juvines having a vent to weake and slow in the first degree to. . . .[2]

A childs vent is quicker than his heat.

An adolescens his vent is equall to his heat.

A juvenis his vent is something slower than his heat.

An old mans vent is slowest of all in reference to his heat. Both his vent and heat are slow.

Whether meats ought to be like to the temperament of these severall ages or whether they ought to be contrary in regard contraria contrariis are prescribed by Physitians to alter any thing that is peccant?

I doe affirme contraria contrariis are not allways to be observed but similia similibus.

[1] MS. Locke, c. 19, ff. 170–6. Locke has written on back: "Medica 75 Sydenham."
[2] Uncompleted sentence in text.

170

Of the 4 constitutions

From the proportion of the vent to the heat doe arise all the internall causes of the 4 constitutions. That which is vented slowest of all is melancholy the next cholerick the next Sanguin that which vents fastest of all is Phlegmaticke by drawing the liquor into the veines before it is concocted. I meane by the proportion ~~of weake & slow heat~~ a weake & slow heat ought to have a weake & slow vent & a strong & quicke heat ought to have a strong & quicke vent. And the same mora or time of venting in our body which hath a strong heat causes mel or choller which in another body which hath a weaker heat causes sang or Phlegme in reference to the degree of heat which concocts as the same aliment may in the space of 3 dayes be incinerated to melancholy or adusted to choller by a strong & violent heat which ~~in by~~ by a temperat heat is only concocted to sanguin & by a weake hardly arrives to Phlegme in that space.

~~And~~

The stronger & quicker the vent to a weake & slow heat the more Phlegmaticke & raw is the constitution.

The more slow ~~&~~ & weake the vent is to a strong & quicke heat the more melancholy is the constitution.

8. The first page of *The Four Constitutions* in Sydenham's handwriting (B.L., MS. Locke, c. 19, f. 170). (*By kind permission of Bodley's Librarian.*)

As for example milke and puerilia are both Phlegmaticke yet hath nature appointed milke and it is the aptest food for children.

But if you should use it to old men or any other youthy spirituose aliments full of heat and moisture it seemes they are more dangerous to them then ether salt meats or meats that are drie and cold of the same likeness to their temper. And this though it be not formally yet per accidens because aliment that is subject to putrefaction as milke etc. putrefies not in a childs body where perhapps it is vented in one day, but in an old mans body or any melancholy body wher the vent is not in 3 dayes it must putrifie or grow sower as milke in a clean pott if you change it every day the pott keeps sweet, if you lett itt stand 3 days it will grow sowre.

Feculency or incineration in the bloud is caused primarily by the boyling of the liquor which evaporatts the sweet spiritts and leaves none but the adust or saline or earthly, so that the drier parts of the bloud are deprived of that dilute and moistning which they had in their primitive originall mixture before those balsamicke and roscid spiritts were deptd.

Secondarily by not venting off the old saline and earthy particles of the bloud in due time as the new comes in, which not venting proceeds from these causes following.

(1) Disproportion of the bigness of the vent to the bigness of the flame whereby ther is more incineration made then can run out at the grate or vent, as in great inflammations of the bloud which hath been long and continued either by often feavers drunkness excessive labor, venery luxury etc. a greater flame hath bin raysed then was appointed by nature for the proportion of the vent and so consequently a small vent which might well according to its primitive intention have vented the ashes of a small flame is not able to cleare of the ashes of a great flame.

(2) Ther being requisitt to the vent not only a passive wideness to lett the ashes through but all so an active attraction, which attraction consists in heat. If the proportion of heat which the part should have fayles of the same either by being too great or to little in its selfe or relatively to other parts the part doth not doe its office. As to the degree of heat in its selfe if the part be colder then nature hath appointed it draws less then nature hath appointed and consequently doth not vent of the ashes as the flames make them.

If the part be too hott itt drawes away too fast from whence these inconveniencies follow.

1st. it drawes faster then the wideness of it selfe can vent. Secondly it draws by its violence humors raw and inconcocted wher by it inflames it selfe and by this inflammation it is incapacitated to ventt at all, upon the totall deprivation of which vent incineration must needs follow. The next consideration is when the heat of the venting part is too great or too little in reference to other parts and that depends upon this principle viz the greater heat allwayes drawes from the less and not the less from the greater. Upon which will follow if the wholl mass of the bloud be inflamed nether the gall spleen gutts reins skin can vent their severall excrements because the wholl bloud draws from them being the more potent heat and not they from it, which is the cause of costivenesse in a feaver and want of sweat so if any particular part be more hott then another part which should vent what is to be vented then that part canott doe its office, as if the reines be to hott for the gutt then these are costive if these are to hott for them then they doe not vent urine sufficiently if the liver be to hott for the spleen then the spleene is nott able to draw off the accid feculency of the bloud and so e contra. If the braine be too hott for the lower parts it causes defluctions by drawing to much juces from the lower parts and so e contra.

So much for the vent of the feculency now we come to the vent of the spiritts.

As there were diseases that depended upon the too quicke orr to slow vent of the feculency etc so are there another series of diseases dependent upon the degree of venting, or not venting the spiritts [as in a berrell of beare if the vent be left open the barrell of beare that is halfe draune the beare will putrifie and the barrell will stincke. In fermentation the barrell will breake if the vessell hath noe vent] under the head of the vent being unproportionably large to the spiritts come all diseases of putrifaction as plauge etc.

Under the head of the vent being unproportionably small to the spiritts come all diseases of firmentation as simple feavers etc.

There is a twofold acidity, the one depends upon the proportion of the vent to the spiritts viz volatile acidity.

This other depends upon the proportion of the vent to the feculency viz fixed acidity. Positive causes are to high fier unproportionable evacuations. Derivitive are evacuations of spiritt by venery excessive exercise bleeding.

Certeyne diseases are incident to old age upon the account of incineration as the goutt stone etc. for the bloud fermenting if it hath bin putte upon a firmentation unproportionably high to natures vents then a little vent hole will not vent the ashes of a large flame or more cinders are made then can be subducted by so small vents. Now nature makes her vent holes proportionable to so much fier only, as it hath appointed life to consist off and is suitable to the carrying on natures functions. [The reason why gout etc are not incident to youth is because any such incineration in youth is prevented by diseases of Putrifaction or feavers etc which comes on from an abundance of inflamable matter and spiritts and plenty of moisture which concurring are apt to inflame before incineration can be made] if the fier hath not burnt so long nor a succession of inflammations.

The salt which is the matter of the gout is a mortified substance and must be therefore vented unless it could be diluted, which cannot be don by any liquidds whatsoever for they can never mix but if it were possible to insunuatt into those adusted particles any subtile moisture or watery spiritt it might be helped by circumvoluting it with oily atomes that it may not bite, or corrode.

The reason why the gout takes the leggs is bicause it being a dull steame and of feculencys apt to descend. The gout is not of that degree of corrosion as to exulcerate the parts as cancers doe but to cause payne only. The wholl old man is an incineration, and ther both bin depredation of spiritts like burnt wine.

If more inflammations have bin made upon the bloud the more incineration is created and consequently diseases come on from that.

It may be experimented whether old wine or burnt in a wooden bottall immerged in a vessell of new wine will alter it to make it like new in tast etc.

Second cause of incineration is defect of naturall heat and spiritts for first by defect of the naturall heat the drier parts of the bloud are deprived of that dilute and moistening which they had in thier originall mixture before those balsamicke and roscid spirit were departed. Secondly the naturall parts through the defect of naturall heat are not able to performe a due attraction wherby much of the feculency would be sucked of. Now loss of this naturall spiritts hath bin made by thier dissipation in immoderatt venery evacuations etc or by suffocation in choaking up natures vent holes by immoderate diett rest and the like.

Note that the gout comes not on till naturall heat begins to decay for as long as the heat was great, nature made some shift notwithstanding the great fermentation and burden.

Nature hath provided milke for infants because thier stomachs have nether heat to burne it as youth have, nor sowerness to putrifie it as age.

The causes of the generation of gouty matter in the bloud was first a succession of inflammations, secondly assimilition as poysons.

The causes of its not being succked off is the want off attraction in the naturall parts wherby much of this feculency would have bin succked off but now is not.

But why should not the gout be incident to all old men who have their bloud thus feculent or adust? I believe as ther are species in generation so thier are not only in putrifaction but even in feculencies.

The reason why exercise is profitable in the gout because it furthers the vent by inducing an equality of attraction in all the parts by stirring up an equall heat that so the matter incinerated is dissipated and vented every way through all the channells as stoole urine transpiration, gall, spleene, every part then vents when it hath attracted. The same doth naturall heat which when it wants it causes want of attraction.

incineration } in both are earth & salt.
feculencye } sulphur is gon & volatile salt.

Primogeniall constitution of gouty men hath bin hott.

Causes of generation of incinerated particles are:

The first incineration was made by inflammation, the second by assimilition without inflammation.

Causes why they are not drawne off when generated in the bloud, the effect doth promote its cause. Incineration caused defect of spiritts, now defect of spiritts in the naturall parts promotes future incineration.

THEOLOGIA RATIONALIS[1]

The question is how far the light of nature, if closely adverted to, may be extended towards the making us good men? Towards the determining of which, this is all that shall be taken for granted by me viz: That he is a wise and thinking man, whosoever he be, that sits upon this Enquiry.

Such a man must needs think thus with himself.

I see that there is a most perfect and exquisite Order in the severall natures of the world, fully conducing to the preservation of their individual Beings, and to the propagation of their kinds: In all which they contribute nothing themselves by their own Counsell or Contrivance, as not knowing how they are made, or how continued in their Beings. And therefore I am enforced to think, that something, which is partaker of admirable wisdom and power is the Contriver and Maker of them. But further considering not only the Artifice by which those particular Bodies which I see and converse with, are made, with respect of each of them to itself. But likewise that Artifice by which each of them hath some subserviency one to another for safeguard, and for other convenience; I am still led into a greater certainty that there was some Supream nature, which (without and differing from all these) did, as he made them so, put them into this order in reference to one another. But extending my thoughts yet further, and considering those innumerable and immense Celestial bodies which I can take in with my natural Eye, and those yet as many more which I can take in by the help of Glasses, and all these put and preservd in Motion so swift and so regular, both for the convenience of each of themselves, and for the conveniency of the whole, as cannot enter into the heart of the wisest man to conceive, how can I less doubt the Being of a nature infinitely wise and infinitely powerfull, by whose contrivance hath been performed and is continued the exquisite order of the stupendous Fabrick of the Universe, then I doubt my own being? And it may be well conceived that the utmost that I can find out by adverting to the

[1] B.M., MS. Sloane 3828, ff. 162–171 verso. There are four versions of *Theologia Rationalis.* The manuscript in the University Library, Cambridge, was published in *Works*, vol. II, Appendix A, but this is several pages shorter than either of the British Museum texts (Add. MS. 6469 and MS. Sloane 3828). There is also a text in the Bodleian Library (MS. Eng. Misc. c. 144, pp. 286–307). All four texts have minor variations of spelling and sometimes of phrasing. Where the variations seem to be significant these are mentioned in a footnote.

great Theatre, bares but a very inconsiderable share in the divine opifice, which is still more exquisite and more great then I (who lye groveling upon the dirt of this Earth) have faculties to comprehend. And tho' by the late discoveries not before known, and by the invention of new arts (such as sailing with a needle touched with a loadstone and others)—which seem altogether impossible to have been lost and to have been found out again (which yet in an infinite series of time they must have been) it is very probable that the world was made in time, and the same of no ancienter date than is assigned unto it: yet admitting the eternity of the world, nevertheless the order thereof (tho' from such eternity) doth no less demonstrate the being of an infinite wisdom and power without it. In a word—there being such order in those particular bodies, whether Sublunary or Celestial, both in reference to one another and to themselves, and not being the least footsteps of Counsell or reason to be found in any of them by which they can contribute anything towards the production of this admirable Order which we call nature; the same must be the contrivance of a wise and powerfull Being, both without them, and in a condition above them, which we call God.

But what am I who thus think? and for what was I made? For, being part of that Universe, which the Supream Artificer hath made, I am to conform to those eternal Lawes, under which he hath constituted my being, which (examining what it is) I find that I am a mixt Animal, partly consisting of rational faculties, and partly of Brutal. But forasmuch as in the scale of Beings I find that the rational faculties are so much more excellent and Superior then Brutal ones, as those are above Vegetables, my chiefest business and the Imployment for which I was sent into the world, is to exert Arts that flow from reason and not from Sense. And these are comprehended under the Obligations in which by the Lawes of my Superior nature I stand to the Supream Being, to human Society and to my Self, consider'd as an Intellectual Creature. For I cannot see how it can possibly be that whilst inferior natures are put under Lawes by which they are determin'd to such or such Operations suitable to the ends of their severall Beings Intellectual Natures only (tho' the very top of divine workmanship) should be put under no Lawes suitable to the ends of their most excellent Beings: but should be left at random, and be as it were Outlawes, in the policy of the world. Wherefore as to the first Obligation incumbent on me as an Intellectual Creature, I consider that neither Air, Fire, Water nor Earth nor the more mixt Bodies, as Mineralls and Vegetables, nor yet the more advanced Compositions of Matter, Brutes, are able to exhibit to the Supream Being that profound adoration which is due to him upon the score of his wisdom and power; and I being the only Creature upon this Globe of Earth, which is my habitation, that am able to do it. It seems to me that I was put here on purpose to be a Contemplator of this his admirable wisdom and power, And that therefore both for my self and for those other inferior Beings which are not endowed with faculties to do it, I am to yield and pay him that profound adoration and Homage which is due to him upon the score of his admirable wisdom and Power.

But now as from the consideration of what I see I am naturally led up into the knowing that there was a divine Architect or Maker of this world, which obliges me to pay my utmost adoration and thanks, so from the same consideration I am engag'd to look up to him for all those things which my nature, whether Intellectual or Brutal stands in need of, and for the diverting all those evills that are contrary to it.

And look how natural it is to me to believe that he gave me my Being, so natural it is to believe that my well being depends upon him, nor can I excise out of my thoughts any more the opinion of the one then of the other, in the way of thinking incident to me as I am a man. And tho' the Supream Being which has so fixt the natural Constitution of the Universe as that it may be unreasonable for me to expect that for my sake and at my request this external establishment should be put out of order, as that being old I should pray for the strength and vigour of youth, or such other things which in the course of nature are put under a necessity of not being able to come to pass, yet it cannot be supposed but that in all events not crossing the establishment of natural constitution he hath preserved to himself the power and disposition of them. As tho' it cannot be, but if I shall be shipwrackt far at sea I must needs be drowned, yet towards the preserving me from this mischief he may be pleased so to dispose the previous Circumstances of my Will and other things, as to prevent my going to Sea, and so in this and in other things he may hinder the Occasions leading to my destruction.

Nor indeed can I entertain any thoughts more derogatory from the Majesty of this divine Being then not supposing him to be a free Agent, but having once put all his works out of his own hands to be concluded within the Limits of his own Establishment hath determin'd irrational Beings to act in some uniform course suitable to the good of themselves and the whole. And tho' he hath set up certain Lights in Intellectual Natures which may direct them to pursue ends suitable to their natures, yet having given these a liberty of Will incident to the very nature of reasonable Beings, he retains his power of inclining or not inclining such Intellectual Natures to pursue courses leading to their wellfare. And truly in the natures of Intellectual Creatures, seems to be the special dominion of the divine Agent: which tho' he doth not determine in their operations as he doth inferior Beings, Yet he doth when he pleaseth, make their Lights set up in their minds more illustrious, or else by a peculiar incitement of thoughts render them more disposed to comply with their own good and to avoid their own unhappiness, so laying in the mean time all the train of Circumstances without them, as that they may conduce to this end.

But now the footsteps of this Moral providence of God, in the world do not seem altogether so visible, as those of his natural, which is clearly discernible in everything that we behold. Yet neither are those totally hid from us, but may be often discovered beyond all reason of doubt in severall Events both relating to whole Countries, and likewise to particular Men: As when God hath design'd any great Revolutions to be made in Kingdoms and States, not only some Person is raised up that is fitted with peculiar Endowments for this work, but an infinite number of Oportunities likewise and Circumstances have at the same time concurr'd to produce this alteration. Nor less may any particular Man be able to trace out the most remarkable footsteps of divine Providence in the course of his own life wherein he will find such and such events which could not be the effects of chance. So many Circumstances and these of different natures having concurr'd towards the production of them as did show that they conspir'd together in this work by some Superior direction. For it is no less in these Moral events then it is in the Works either of nature or Art in which if we see so great train of things all concurring to the same end, we reasonably believe they made not themselves or came by chance, but were effected by some Intelligent Agent. But how certain soever we may be that such Moral Events in matters of Fact did proceed from a Superior direction, yet we cannot understand the final Causes of them they being hid in the mind of the Supream Being, who had preserv'd to himself the Prerogative of overruling the Moral establishment of the World, as he pleaseth, and therefore are past all reach of human wit,[1] whilst many times we cannot but perceive that all things happen indifferently, and the same things to fools as to wise, to good as to bad; which things yet are not the effect of chance, but of a Superior direction. And tho' all such events have had Causes Suitable to their production: Yet have not Causes their Events alwayes suited to them. As tho' Riches generaly speaking are acquir'd by industry; and health by Temperance, yet

[1] "Will" in B.M., Add. MS. 6469.

industrious men happen often to be poor, and Intemperate to be healthy.

Wherefore to this eternal infinitely good, wise and powerful Being, as I am to pay all that adoration thanks and Worship which I can rise up in my mind unto, So to him, from the Consideration of this his Providence, whereby he doth govern the World, my Self, and all things therein, I am pura integra et incorrupta mente, to pray for all that good, which is necessary for my mind and Body and for diverting all those Evills, which are contrary to their natures: above all, desiring that my mind may be endow'd with all maner of vertue. But in requesting things relating to my Body and its Concerns, having alwayes a deference to the Will of the Supream Being, who knows what is best for me better than I do my Self. And tho' my requests relating to these bodily Concerns of mine are not answer'd: Nevertheless herein I worship him, by declaring my dependence upon him.

And for as much as that in many respects I have transgress'd his divine lawes written upon my nature, I am humbly to implore his pardon, it being as natural for me to do it as it is to implore the pardon of a man whom I know I have offended. In all which requests of mine and all his Creatures, how many how so ever they be in number, and how distant so ever they be in place, he being infinite, is as ready at hand to hear and to help, as any man, who is but finite is at hand to administer food to his Child that craves it.

Next considering my Self to be part of Common nature of mankind hew'd as it were out of the same block, and likewise out of gratitude to the comon Father of us all, I find myself engaged not to hurt, but by all the means I can to benefit mankind.

And for as much I am so made that I cannot preserve my Self in my being without the help and assistance of others, my condition being above that of Brutes, who stand in need only of those few things which the Earth of its own accord doth yield to them, and for as much also as I am not able to defend my Self from the Injuries which those of own kind led by pride, anger, Covetousness and such like Brutish Passions may do to me, I find my Self engaged to comply with the Lawes of human Society, which is the Bond, by which the good of men is held together, and to fill up the severall Duties of my condition in reference to that Society.

Lastly concerning the Obligations under which I stand in reference to my Self, I consider that in this Conjunction of my Intellectual and Brutal nature, for as much as I find my Soul to be far more excellent Being than my Body, I am to preserve entire to my mind, the Dominion which is given to it over my Body in repressing the Sensual appetitions thereof, which are against my reason. Nor less am I to preserve to it in all other things, its own Dignity, not permitting any labes dedecoris to cleave to it, not suffering it to be dejected, when things without me, and which are not in my power go cross to me, nor to be vainly elated when things of the like nature succeed, in regards that neither adversity make me a worse man, nor prosperity a better. And tho' because I consist likewise of a Body whose appetitions I am not to Contradict when they are not against my reason, If I might have my choice I desire a prosperous condition, yet when I am under Circumstances of misery which seem vile and contemptible to fools, even in this I have an Oportunity to exhibit a Specimen of the Excellency of my Superior nature by Suffering with patience those Evills, there being not in the whole world a more glorious Spectacle, then the seeing a good man oppressed with great and insuperable difficulties, and yet bearing them with patience as things which happen promiscuously to good and bad men in the frame and Constitution under which the Supream Being hath put all earthly things, and as being by no means hurtfull to any particular man whilst they are good for the whole.

And this Contemplation of the Excellency of my mind above my Body, as it is productive of the vertues last mentioned, so it is of this also, that I embrace verity in all my words, as discerning the comeliness there is, in making my tongue to be the faithfull Interpreter of my mind, and the turpitude that there is in causing it to bely the same.

Also from the same Consideration it is that I am neither to think Speak or Act anything that is indecorous or disgracefull to this divine Inmate, whose excellency above my body nature has tacitly pointed out by impressing upon me a Verecundia or being ashamed of many Actions of my Body, which therefore I hide from those of my own Species.

But now forasmuch as I consist likewise of a Body which is submitted to the same Conditions with other Animals of being nourished and propagating my Kinde, and likewise which wants many other Conveniences of Cloathing Housing and the like, which their nature requires not, all those likewise are to be respected by me according to my severall wants, but still with a Subserviency to my reason, which is my Superior part, and Acts flowing from the same, my chiefest business, as an Ambassador who is sent into a forreign Country is not sent to eat and drink, tho' he is inforced to do both.

This seems to be my nature, and these the Lawes imprinted on it in obeying of which do consist Acts of vertue, and in disobeying them those of vice. But now tho' I must thus think or not think at all, yet forasmuch as I find my Self to be strongly diverted from obeying those Lawes written upon my Intellectual nature, by the Suggestions of my sensual part, which are apt to corrupt my reason by their enticements, and seem to bid fairer in many Important necessities of life for acceptance than the other, therefore I enquire whether there be no assistance to be had for my mind, by which it may grapple with my body, and by which it, and all the Concerns thereof may be subservient only to her Self and to her more excellent end, which is to obey those divine Lawes: I find that to excite my mind and to encourage it in this Conflict, I have great reason to believe that when I dye I shall not extinguish, but that there shall abide to my better part a condition of happiness or misery suitable to my having lived in conformity to the Lawes abovementioned or having liv'd otherwise.

How my soul, which I look upon to be an immortal Being in me, that is the Principle of thinking, should extinguish with my Body I cannot in any reasonable way of thinking conceive. But that it is immaterial appears hence. Vizt. that the immediate Actions thereof which are thinking have not the least affinity with matter, nor often do those Actions when exerted terminate in it. As when I think of time, or when I think this present thought which is my present subject Vizt. that my soul is immaterial. And indeed most of those Ideas which the art of Logick in the whole Latitude thereof furnishes me withall are totally removed from matter, and yet are so necessary that unless I have them either by nature or art I cannot think true without them. If it shall be thought that whatsoever is must needs be material, and whatsoever is not so must be nothing at all: I would enquire whether by matter we do not understand that which is the Object of some one or other of our senses? If so whether there be not many things in the Universe that come not under any sense that we are endowed with? For suppose an Oyster has the faculty of reasoning, ought he then to conclude, because nature has endowed him with that one sense of tasting, and perhaps with that other of touching, therefore there were no other Objects in the world then those which answered to his two senses? So to think were to be more like an Oyster than a Man, who must needs suppose that it is not only possible but likely also, that in the Universe there are an infinite number of Beings which by no mean come under his five senses, but which nevertheless are the Objects of other senses, with which other Creatures may be endowed, among which Beings more may be incorporeal then those which partake of matter: which things tho' I cannot know to be so, yet I can conceive better then I can how all things in the Universe can be one nature only to wit matter. And cannot I by an easy train of thoughts conceive immaterial Beings? when I conceive how much finer Air is than Earth, and how much Aether than Air, till at length I rest in something, which is removed altogether from matter, and yet no less a Being than that? or is it more difficult for me to think that the immense Interspaces between the Globes, whether Suns or Planets, up and down in the Expanse of the Universe (which bear no proportion to the Globes themselves) are perfectly disjunct from matter? these being thrown down, and constituting the gross Substance of such Globes and the substance of those exhalations which Issue from them and proceed no great way above them, and that in such Interspaces may reside infinite more species of immaterial natures, altogether free from any mortal filth, then there are material ones residing upon the Globes themselves. But however this be I am sure 'tis difficult to conceive how so almost divine a thing as thinking can proceed from matter, with which it seems to have the least Correspondence. And the Brutes (whose Being we constitute only under mater) seem to put forth Actions flowing from thinking, yet whether these Actions are not only the effect of their parts consisting of such matter, and so put together by the divine Artificer, as that they are determined in the very principles of the Mechanic, to such and such actions, knowing not what they do, is not altogether so impossible as may be thought, forasmuch as we find that a great many of those actions of theirs, which being in order to certain ends, do look like the results of thinking yet are not so. As that the severall species of Birds should begin to build their nests for the repositing their Young just before the time wherein they are to bring forth and those nests so built both in respect of place and likewise of Materials as generally speaking is most convenient to the nature and safeguard of their Young, and that with so much artifice that the most cunning Mechanick that can be found amongst mankind cannot imitate, this may be thought an effect flowing from Ratiocination, but yet if we consider that those Birds which were hatcht but the last season should the next year without any Instructions from the Old ones rude and inexperienc'd build such nests with such curiosity of artifice as did the old ones, we must needs think that these actions of theirs flow from the make of their Bodies and nothing else. That a Hen should sit so long upon her Eggs seems to me to be an effect of some kind of thought in her by which she designs the hatching of them and the bringing forth of her young. Which act of Incubation nevertheless she will exert at certain seasons whether she have eggs under her or no. That a chick as soon as hatched should at the sight of a Kite run into a hole or to the Hen for its protection as if it had been long furnished with experience and knowledge of that Birds being used to devour those of its species. That so low and despicable a Creature as an Earthworm who lives in and upon the Earth and is but little in its nature advanced above it, should have such a Contrivance for its safeguard and Habitation as working holes in the Earth and should with a wonderful sagacity quit the same, crawling up upon the surface thereof when at any time it feels the Motion of the Earth that is made either by Moles that live upon their species or any other Motion made by digging with a spade resembling the Motion made by Moles, and according to its power shifting for itself, no less then a man would out of a house which is on fire. And how can we conceive that this acting tho' in order to so reasonable an end in so vile and contemptible a Creature should proceed from thoughts or that it should have any at all. 'Twere endless to mention in Flies and other Insects such Instincts. Now tho' in Doggs, Foxes, and some other animals we perceive acts which seem nearer to resemble Ratiocination, yet nevertheless we may reasonably think that if a train of actions to an orderly end may flow from the Mechanic of other animals, such higher operations which these exert, do result likewise from the Bodies consisting of such Materials and so contrived by the divine Artificer, as that they shall produce actions suited to their nature, they in the mean time neither knowing nor perceiving that they are doing relating to the end for which they do it, any more than my Kidneys whilst they are separating the serous part of my blood. But however herein is to be perceived the stupendous wisdom of the divine Artificer. That matter alone so put together, should produce operations in those animals so nearly resembling that of Intelligent Beings.

If it be objected that when such actions in Brutes proceed from mere matter, and we know not the ultima potentia materiae why may not the action of thinking in men proceed from the matter only? This I confess I should be very inclinable to believe could I be assured that Brutes did at all think. And tho' we do not know the utmost power of matter, yet we do the utmost power of what we can conceive, and we cannot conceive that matter should think. But tho' it be more hard for the Principles of natural science to draw Conclusions that are demonstrable of the immortality of the soul, for as much as the soul itself can no more discern it self, save by its operations, then the eye can do the eye, and also for as much as this science from whence it should derive its information is either none at all or very little, showing us only things as they consist in matter of fact, and not leading us up into the Causes and efficiencies: Yet there is another and that in my opinion a more true way of thinking, grounded upon Moral Science (the Principles of which tho' not of the other, mankind is endowed with faculties to comprehend) which will make it not only easy to think that the soul is immortal, but hard to conceive how it should be otherwise. For when I consider that the infinite Governor of the Universe hath so made me that in my Intellect I have some small Glimpses of his Being, whilst I cannot but apprehend that immensity of Power and of wisdom which is in him and doth appear in whatever I see, and this I must apprehend if I endeavour not to do it, it being closely riveted, and as it were coessential to my nature, or if I have gotten the knowledge of it by hear say only, it being so fitted to my nature that I must needs believe it, which two make up the same thing. Now how can I think that this divine Being that hath admitted me to this little acquaintance with him will let the laying down of my Body perfectly break off this acquaintance, and not rather that the throwing off of this Load of Corruption will put my soul into a condition more suitable to its own nature it being much more difficult to think how such a noble substance as the soul should be united to the Body than how it should subsist separately from it. But add to this that I have not only Faculties of knowing this divine Being, but in compliance with him, I have ador'd him with all the attention I could screw up my heavy mind unto, and have endeavour'd to yield obedience to those Lawes which he hath written upon my nature: That I who have done this (supposing that I have done it) should extinguish when my body dyes, is yet more unlikely. Moreover I consider, that this matter of the Universe hath brought all his ends so together, that he hath implanted no affections upon the meanest animal, but hath made Objects to answer them, as he that hath made the eye hath made Colours, and he that hath made the Organs of hearing hath likewise made sounds, and so of an infinite number of other affections not only in Animals, but even in those natures inferior to them all, which have Objects suited to them, and if they had not, there would be a flaw even in the Constitution of the Universe, which cannot be charg'd upon the infinitely wise Creator. But now that there should be found in mankind a certain appetition or reaching out after a future happiness, and that there should be no such thing to answer to it, but that this Cheat should be put upon the rational part of Man, which is the highest nature in this Globe where we live, is to me very improbable. And Contemplating the perfection of the divine Wisdom and goodness, seems altogether impossible. But if it be objected that such an appetition in us may proceed from our Pride, in thinking too well of our selves and that no footsteps thereof have been found in some Nations, and in some particular men of other Nations where such appetition has obtained, and therefore is not connatural and born with us; Let it be consider'd that tho' there may be some such whole Nations so immersed in immanity and brutishness, (which yet I find not sufficiently prov'd) and admit that there are some particular men here and there in other civilized Countries, who either by Sensuality have immersed themselves into the same Brutishness or else through pride have endeavour'd to soar above other men, but through that weakness which is always incident to wit without wisdom, have lost their faculty of right reasoning: yet if the Bulk of Mankind which no man will question, have upon the opinion of a future state reached out after it in those divers Methods and Ways that their severall Religions and Customs or reason did suggest unto them to be the best means of attaining the same, then it is a sign that if this Notion be not connatural to man (which yet I think it to be) yet it carryes with it such a Suitableness to our reason, that where ever it hath been started it hath been complyed with, which is all one as if it had been connatural. And which is more, by how much whole Countries or particular men have been civiliz'd and endow'd with greater endowments of Understanding then other Countries or other particular men, by so much they have indulg'd to this opinion that there is a future Estate, surpassing them, as in other parts of Understanding so likewise in this true thinking.

Furthermore it is of no small weight towards proving the immortality of the soul. That there being not sufficient retribution made for the greatest vertues or vices in this life, there must needs be a future State, wherein that just respect will be had to good and bad men which is fit.

That there is no such retribution in this world is manifest when consulting Histories of former times or making use of our own observations, we find that bad men many times enjoy a great affluence of Comforts, and good men are oppress'd with all kinds of misery. And sometimes these wicked men do owe all their Enjoyments even to their wickedness, and those good men their misery to their treading strictly in the Pathes of vertue. What shall we say to those great men, who without any other motive then the getting a great name in the world have by fire and sword destroyed whole Countries of innocent men? who could be no otherwise aggressors then as they desired to breath in the Common air and to eat the Fruits of their Land, which with hard labour their own hands had Cultivated? These great men nevertheless have liv'd like Gods upon Earth everywhere honour'd and swimming in all worldly pleasures, and at length dying upon their Beds, leave their ill gotten possessions to their Children. What shall we say likewise to private Persons who by violating the Wills of the dead by obtaining[1] Trusts and by oppressing Orphans and Widows, and by

[1] Latham in *Works*, vol. II, Appendix A, reads "betraying".

sundry other frauds in their Dealings have heaped up great Estates, and have thereby exempted themselves from that misery and want which others have undergone, that have not given themselves the liberty of being unjust tho' they have had oportunities, which might have entitled them to the same getting? Nor can it be said that my being well pleas'd and inwardly satisfied with my Self with my doing well is a sufficient reward for the good actions which I have done against my own Interest, nor the Consciousness of my own Guilt a sufficient punishment for the wickedness I have committed towards the accommodating my pleasures. For I will demand of any man why (prescinding from the consideration of a future state) would I embrace vertue rather than vice at all times, and in the whole latitude of them? tho' generally speaking I will allow that he who embraceth Justice, Temperance, Chastity &c. shall more consult his own good as to his present being then he that practiceth the Contrary Vices, (Reputation in the world which is the foundation of Riches and health attending those, and dishonour poverty and sickness commonly attending these) yet this doth not alwayes hold. What then? is it for fear of the Lawes that men ought to forbear vice? What argument can that be? that a Tyrant who Rules far and near and abounding in power and wealth is superior to all his neighbours should not oppress when he pleaseth? is it the Torment of Conscience that is said to vex bad men that should keep men from flagitious acts? what then should deterr men, who by a series of wicked actions, have quite extinguished all such sense of Evill? or else perhaps who through sottishness of nature never had it. Is it, according to the Stoicks, vice, as vice, or the turpitude thereof, should keep men from wickedness? what turpitude is there in vice to him that thinks it not so, how much soever may be thereof in a man that takes other measures by the Rules of vertue? Is fear[1] of dishonour poverty or sickness or some other hurt to himself, are there not an infinite number of Cases wherein a man has oportunity to Commit flagitious acts, with impunity to himself as to all these Inconveniencies? and be so far from hurting himself, that he shall satisfy the most important desires of sensual life? and admitting that he knowes it to be an evill action which he commits, yet the advantage which he reaps to himself thereby shall bid fairer for his Closing with his Villany, then his being conscious to himself that he has offended, shall bid towards the deterring him from it: and so turning the Tables, that which is the cause of vice is also of vertue; The reward which is propos'd to it by them who have writ entire Volumes of Moral Philosophy, being not a satisfactory ground for enforcing the rules thereof. Amongst which Tully (whose profundity

[1] Latham's text finishes here.

of wisdom I cannot however but almost adore) is short, in his Offices, of that rational end which a man should propose to himself for his encouragement to tread in the narrow and strict paths of vertue. For whilst he tells me that vertue is propter se expetibilis (upon the reason of which Principle he grounds all the Rules of his manners and good life) what can he mean, but that it pleaseth a man? but if it pleaseth not him whom I would perswade to be vertuous, what argument can I use to him? and what, tho' that excellent Author present me with a fair draught of the Duty of man? yet he leaves me void of Understanding that end why I should put his Principles in use. If he objects to me (as he doth all along in his excellent piece de Legibus) that the vertues which I embrace with respect to my own profit, are mercenary, which destroys the very essence of those vertues as in the instance he gives of Justice, liberality, friendship and the rest, I acknowledg they are not mercenary, but gratuitous where they are pleasing to me; [but where they are not pleasing][1] what motive is there to me to embrace them?

Wherefore by what has been said, it doth plainly appear that altho' the Lawes of nature are written upon our minds so clearly that he who hath not defaced them by sensuality may easily read them, Yet the rewards and punishments that in this world are due to the keeping or breaking them, do not alwayes appear. But now if there are such sanctions established in the very minde of man, and by such a Supream Governor, and there be neither reward nor punishment, what then is become of that Government which we are reasonably to suppose is in the world? Ut enim (says Tully to another purpose) nec domus nec Respublica ratione quadam et Disciplina designata videatur, si in ea nec recte factis Praemia exstent ulla, nec supplicia peccatis: sic mundo divina in homines moderatio profecto nulla est, si in ea nullum est discrimen bonorum et malorum.

But there are such Lawes written upon our nature, it being absurd to think that whilst all inferior Beings do obey the Lawes of their several natures, the highest natures should have no Lawes at all to conform themselves to, and consequently that there is Order in those, and nothing but Confusion in these. Wherefore there must be a divine Regimen belonging to the world, and that consists not only in the Order which all Beings whether inanimate or Brutal do exert by vertue of their Being so made at first, that they should act in such an Order with respect to the whole, or themselves; But in ordering Intellectual natures also to act suitable to the Lawes of their more excellent Being. But these being endow'd with the Prerogative of Free

[1] Supplied from the other version in B.M., Add. MS. 6469.

Will above inferior natures, and being not determined by a natural[1] necessity to act thus or thus, like other inferior Beings, are capable only of vertue or vice, by governing themselves according to the Lawes of their nature, which is their Reason, or by deviating from it, and have a Science connatural to them, whereby they know when they have done well or ill, which we call Conscience; and as there cannot be wanting certain Lawes to make up this divine Regimen over Rational Beings so there cannot be wanting rewards and punishments in another State.

If it shall be objected that the directing all our actions to our own profit (altho' the same is to be reaped in another life) makes all our vertues not gratuitous but mercenary, and so instead of being good we are cunning men, I would ask these two things. First whether it be any disparagement to us to receive the divine benignity? That continuation of our Being, and all that happiness belonging to it? For if we consider that infinite disproportion that is between him and us, we cannot think our selves ungenerous, who deriving all from him are content in everything that we do to procure his favour, no more than we can think it baseness in a Beggar to receive an Almes from the greatest King.

Secondly can it be[2] expected that mankind who is partly rational and partly brutal should be so perfect as that from the very Idea of vertue men should stedfastly and closely embrace it without needing the enticements or Terrors of hope and fear? and in the concernment of his Reason lay aside those Passions that are so riveted into his nature, and are so necessary for him in the Conduct of all his affairs, that he can scarce govern himself without them? He that thinks so hath a mind above his Fortune. Add to this that self preservation is a Law written upon the nature of all Beings as deeply as anything else.

This is the Scheme of the nature of mankind, and of the Lawes co-essential to his nature, quae saeculis omnibus ante nata quam scripta Lex ulla aut quam omnino Civitas[3] constituta, and is not particular to this or that Country, but Universal. Altho' yet mankind from the weakness and imperfection incident to the Low condition wherein, in the Order of Intellectual Beings he stands, is apt to be led aside into one of the two Extreams of Atheism or Superstition, and consequently is liable to mistakes both in his principles and practices. Nam ut vere loquamur, Superstitio, fusa per gentes oppressit omnium fere animos, atque hominum imbecillitatem occupavit. Nec vero (id enim diligenter intelligi volo) Superstitione tollenda Religio tollitur; nam et majorum constituta tueri sacris Ceremoniisque retinendis sapientis est. Et esse

[1] "real" in B.M., Add. MS. 6469.
[2] "Reasonably" is added here in B.M., Add. MS. 6469.
[3] "veritas" in B.M., Add. MS. 6469.

presentem aliquam aeternamque naturam, et eam suspiciendam admirandamque Hominum generi, pulchritudo mundi, ordoque Celestium rerum cogit confiteri. Quamobrem ut Religio propaganda etiam est, quae est juncta cum cognitione naturae: Sic Superstitionis stirpes omnes ejiciendae sunt. Tull: de Divin:

Correspondence

May 12, 1651.[1]

Council of State to the Army Committee

The troops of Capt. Ivory, Capt. Ayers, Lieut. Clements, Capt. Sydenham, Major Warren, Capt. Jenkins Jones, and Capt. Moyse, being part of 3,000 horse raised out of the militia forces, and being now appointed to march upon service, cannot proceed there to until they be entered on to pay, and be enabled by the advance of some part of it. That there may be no delay, you are to issue warrants to the Treasurers-at-War for the payment of so much to them as you judge fit to enable them to march, and for the future, to take care that they be paid equally with the rest of the forces upon the Establishment.

Whitehall. May 12, 1651.[2]

Council of State to the Militia Commissioners of Essex

We formerly wrote you for a proportion of horse to be raised out of your militia horse, and as you are yet deficient of 26 of them, we desire you to send them forthwith to Capt. Sydenham that he being complete, may attend the service of the commonwealth to which he is commanded, and which cannot bear delay.

May 16, 1651.[3]

Council of State to Col. Rich

We have thought fit, in order to securing the Midland parts, that you should march down to Leicester or Nottingham, and lie in the parts thereabouts, with 3 troops of horse of your own regiment, Major Horsman's, Capt. Brewster's, Capt. Sydenham's, Capt. Moody's and the dragoons of Capt. Laurences, and Capt. Chaplain. Disperse yourselves so as to be ready to answer any emergency and keep up a constant correspondence with Major-General Harrison, and from time

[1] C.S.P. (Dom.), 1651, p. 195. [2] *Ibid.*, p. 191. [3] *Ibid.*, p. 204.

to time advertise us of the state of affairs there, so that you may with expedition receive such orders as may be required.

CAPTAIN SYDENHAM'S PETITION[1]

To his Highness the Lord Protector of England, Scotland, and Ireland etc.

The humble petition of Capt. Thomas Sydenham.

Sheweth:

That there was due to my brother, Major John Sydenham, slayne in Scotland, a very considerable arrear for sundry and constant services in England and Ireland.

That your Highness Petitioner besides that he was legally entitled to the sayd arrears did furnish his sayd brother with divers sums of money to inable him to buy horses and other necessaries for his going to Scotland for which your petitioner was never satisfied.

That the severall papers which should certifie the aforementioned services, being all lost upon the death of the sayd Major Sydenham together with what else he had, your petitioner was made incapable in the ordinary way to recover what was due.

That your Highness petitioner after two years attendance on the Parliament for satisfaction, did applie himselfe to a Committee newly constituted for receiving petitions, who upon examination of his case did order that Mr. Carie Rawligh should report their sense to the Parliament, which was that satisfaction should be made him out of Irish lands, but your petitioner not being able to get on the Report till those Lands were passed away to Act, would not enjoy the benefit of that order.

Your petitioner therefore most humbly prayes your Highness that your Highness will please in consideration of the faythfull and valiant services of your petitioners sayd brother, to order such satisfaction as in your Highness piety and wisdom shall be thought fit to be made to your petitioner, who hath likewise himselfe faithfully served the Parliament with the loss of much bloud and therby much disabled his body, for all which yet he never sued for any satisfaction. Your petitioner would likewise insist on the many services of another brother of his, one Major Francis Sydenham, slayne in the West, whose executors never received more than eighty pounds satisfaction of his arrears; but your petitioner shall cease to trouble your Highness.

And your petitioner shall pray etc.

Thomas Sydenham.

[1] P.R.O., S.P. Interregnum, vol. lxvii, f. 37. Printed in C.S.P. (Dom.) 1654, p. 14. Printed by S. Gee, *St. Bartholomew's Hospital Reports* (1883), **19**, 2–4, and J. F. Payne, *op. cit.*, pp. 72–4 and p. 81.

Friday March 3rd, 1653.
Endorsed—Not relievable after 25 March.
Capt. Sydenham's Petn.
ref. 8 March } 53
ref. 16 March } 54

Friday, March 3, 1653–4.

His Highness being very sensible of the matters represented in this petition, is pleased in an especial manner, to recommend it to the Council that they may give the petitioner due satisfaction, and that with all convenient expedition.

(Signed) J. Sadler.

14 March 1653/4.[1]

Order on request from the Committee on Capt. Thos. Sydenham's petition, that £600 should be ordered him in full of all demands, to be settled where it shall not be burdensome on the Treasuries, and that the Revenue Committee should give him such employment as he is most capable of—that the former Committee consider where the £600 can be best charged, and recommend him to the Revenue Committee.

25 April, 1654.[2]

Hall order on report of Capt. Thos. Sydenham's petition that the £600 ordered be paid out of £811–14–1d received by Geo. Dawson and Thos. Errington, of Newcastle, Commissioners for public debts, and remaining in their hands as collectors of an imposition on coals in Newcastle, and that they pay it accordingly.
Approved 4 May, and warrant signed 11 May, 1654.

Sydenham to Robert Boyle[3]

Pall-Mall, April 2, 1668.

Sir,

It had becomed me to have begged your acceptance, when I took the boldness to tender to you the second edition of my book;[4] but

[1] C.S.P. (Dom.), 1654, p. 33.
[2] *Ibid.*, p. 115.
[3] Robert Boyle, *Works* (1772), vol. VI, pp. 648–50; J. F. Payne, *op. cit.*, pp. 239–42; Thomas Sydenham, *Works* (1848), pp. lxxii–iv.
[4] *Methodus Curandi Febres* etc. (1666), dedicated to Boyle. The second edition appeared in 1668 prefixed with a Latin poem by Locke in praise of the author's methods.

partly business, and partly an unwillingness in me to give you two troubles at once, diverted me from writing. But now that you are pleased to give yourself the pains of a thanks, which I never thought myself capable of deserving from you, I hold myself obliged to return you my humble thanks, that you take in good part my weak endeavours, and are pleased to have a concern (as you always have done) for me. I perceive my friend Mr. Locke hath troubled you with an account of my practice, as he hath done himself in visiting with me very many of my variolous patients especially. It is a disease, wherein as I have been more exercised this year than ever I thought I could have been, so I have discovered more of its days than ever I thought I should have done. It would be too large for a letter, to give you an account of its history; only in general I find no cause, from my best observation, to repent of anything said by me in my tract De Variolis, but do greatly, that I did not say, that, considering the practices that obtain, both amongst learned and ignorant physicians, it had been happy for mankind, that either the art of physic had never been exercised, or the notion of malignity never stumbled upon. As it is palpable to all the world, how fatal that disease proves to many of all ages, so it is most clear to me, from all the observations that I can possibly make, that if no mischief be done either by physician or nurse, it is the most slight and safe of all other diseases. If it shall be your hap to be seized of that disease (as probably you never may) I should recommend to you, upon the word of a friend, the practice mentioned in the 155th page of my book. I confess, some accidents there are incident to that disease, which I was never able to master, till towards the end of last summer, and which therefore could not be mentioned by me, as a phrenitis coming on the eighth day, where the patient is in the vigour of his youth, hath not been blooded, and hath been kept in a dose from his first decumbiture; as likewise (which is wont to be no less fatal) a great dosing, accompanied with a choaking respiration, coming on from the tenth day (reckoning from the rigour and horror, which is my way of accounting) and occasioned by the matter of a ptyalism in a fluxpox, baking & growing thick, as it declines & comes to concoction in those days. But, which is observable, the small-pox never fluxes or runs together, but it hath been thrust out before the fourth day; and where you see any eruption the first, second, or third day from the decumbiture, you may safely pronounce it will be a flux-pox, or a measle, for that sort in its first appearance is like it; and, which is likewise observable in the highest flux of all, as that which comes out the first or second day, it is in vain to endeavour the raising them to a height, for it is both impossible, and unsafe to attempt, but all the discharge that can be, must be either from a ptyalism, in a grown person, or a diarrhoea, in an infant, to whom the same is no more dangerous than the other to the former. And wherever they flux, their discharge must be made one of those two ways. But of these things, I shall discourse to you more at large, when I shall have the happiness to see you, which I hope may be suddenly. The town stands well in health, and at our end not anybody sick, that I hear, of the small-pox. I have much business about other things, and more than I can do, who yet am not idle. I have the happiness of curing my patients, at least of having it said concerning me, that few miscarry under me; but cannot brag of my correspondency with some other of my faculty, who, notwithstanding my profoundness in palmistry and chemistry, impeach me of great insufficiency, as I shall likewise do my taylor, when he makes my doublet like a hop-sack, and not before, let him adhere to what hypothesis he will. Though yet in taking fire at my attempts to reduce practice to a greater easiness and plainness, and in the mean time letting the mountebank at Charing-cross[1] pass unrailed at, they contradict themselves, and would make the world believe I may prove more considerable than they would have me. But to let these men alone to their books, I have again taken breath, and am pursuing my design of specifics, which, if but a delusion, so closely haunts me, that I could not but indulge the spending of a little money and time at it once more. I have made a great progress in the thing, and have reason to hope not to be disappointed. My occasions will not suffer me to give you more trouble, and therefore be pleased to accept of the tender of those very unfeigned thanks, which I here make you, for all the singular kindnesses and favours whereby you have obliged me to be very uncomplimentally,

SIR,

Your most humble servant,

T. SYDENHAM.

Sydenham to John Locke[2]

I conceave itt by noe meanes saff for his Lordshipp[3] to stopp up the abscess, triall once having bin made of the unsuccessfullness of doing it and the flux of matter as yett seeming too much in proportion to the canale, and I judge it better to keepe it open with a silver pipe then a wax candle, in regard that from the use of a candle the matter will

[1] This is a reference to Richard Talbor, an apothecary and unlicensed practitioner.

[2] P.R.O., 30/24/47/2, ff. 9–10. Superscribed by Locke "Consilium Abscessus, Dr. Sydenham, '68". Partly printed by Sir William Osler in *Lancet*, 1900, **ii**, 10.

[3] Lord Ashley, later first Earl of Shaftesbury.

have the less opportunity to issue out and consequently the passage choak up. But I think 'twere better that the pipe were shorter because by the present length thereof his Lordshipp is liable to dangerous accidents following any unequal motion of the body which in process of time may easily happen from riding in a coach, stouping or the like; nor doth it seeme to be suspected that the matter will not worke itselfe out when the orifice shall be kept open. I conceive itt may somewhat contributt to the discharge of the matter if my Lord shall lie on his left side[1] or as much as he can and in regard the imposthume is depending if he shall lie with his upper parts low. I hold itt very unsaff to use injections of any sort because the cavity being depending, the liquor how agreeable soever in other respects will by lodging it selfe in any little cavities begett new impostumations to which those injections administer matter and by this meanes the cavity still enlarged. I should thinke that a drying drinke constantlye kept to for ordinary drinke would be more conducible to the drying up of this flux of matter and sweetening the whole mass of bloud and humors than anything whatsoever: Nor doe I conceave that my Lord's spare habitt of body may discourage from this course, but rather contrary when 'tis notoriouslye knowne that a drying diett though used with greater severity than 'twill be necessary to putt my Lord upon, hath after a while rendered bodies that before were very emaciated now plumpe and vigorouse. But what 2 draughts in a day can signifie, and those too of a liquor so compounded that the greater respect is had to the uncerteyne and conjecturall virtue of sanitives and the lesser to the certeyne and sensible qualitie of Driers I cannot imagine.

This therefore with submission to those that know more I should advise.

That nothing be don to the part saveing the use of a pipe that may be made somewhat shorter or to be lengthened with a wax candle and that it be dressed once a day if the matter be much, once in 2 days if little.

That of the stronger sort of liquor halfe a pint be taken hott every morning 1 hour before his Lordshipp riseth, and the same quantity at night as soon as he is in his bedd.

That the smaller liquor be constantly drunke at his meales and at other times cold.

That he purge or take a clyster every 5th or 6th day. Lett his Lordshipp's diett be in proportion to this way att least lett suppinges be avoided.

[1] Sydenham wrote "right side", which was crossed out by Locke who inserted "left side" instead.

The stronge liquor

Take of lime, 1 pound; throw it into a gallon of boyling hott water. When this hath stood and is cold scum itt; throw off the cleare and add to itt of other water one gallon more. Of Sarsaparilla 4 ounces. Burdock rootes 2 ozs. Of China, santalum citrinum, lignum lentissimum, sassaphras, liquirish, raisons of the sun stoned of each one oz. Off shavings of harts horne and Cardus seedes of each halfe an ounce. Leafes of agrimony, speedwell, sanicle and the tops of Snt Johnswort of each one handfull. Infuse these all night together in a diett pott over hott embers. The next morning boyle them to the consuming of a third part. Then strayne it through a woollen cloth, and put it by in a cold place, in earthen bottles. You may make halfe the quantity at a time.

The smaller liquor

Is to be made of the same quantity of ingredients but a double quantity of water and without lime.

Mr. William Sydenham to Dr. Thomas Sydenham[1]

(For my honoured Uncle Dr. Sydenham in London)
(in Dorsetshire)
Winford Eagle Novemb. 19. 1675

Honoured Sir,

Yours I recieved wherby I understood of your kindnes towards me—by using your Interest with Mr. Savill to keepe me from the office of Sheriff for which I most heartily thanke you, and shall alwayes owne you to be the only relation living from whom I have recieved signall tokens of kindnes and respect. I intend to returne my thankes to my honoured friend Mr. Savill for his great kindnesse in this affaire. I shall be very glad to be honoured with your correspondence. By your last I percieve you have a booke in the Presse.

I thinke in my last I did informe you of my uncle Lees[2] and coson Chidleighs reterne for Devon again; I'le acquaint you with a thing which I thinke strange, whilst my coson Chidleighs were here, shee being a great lover of Antiquities, desired me and as I formerly promised her, to have one of the Roman barrowes to bee digged up as you know on the Downes are plenty in this County especially. Wherefore I caused one to be digged, and found nothing in it but black Cinders

[1] B.L., MS. Gen. Top., c. 25, f. 33 (Aubrey's collection of notes for his *Monumenta Britannica*).

[2] Mary, Thomas Sydenham's eldest sister, married Richard Lee of Winslade.

like Smyths coale, which was just at their goeing (for Devon) but I promised I would try twenty more ere I found something to satisfie her curiositie. Some of my workmen advised me to digge up the Barrow in a ground if you remember it called Ferndowne nigh the sheepe-house in the Roade goeing to Bridport and my men offered me that if there was nothing in it they would loose their dayes hire, which I greed to, and on they goe, and when they had cast away the earth it was full of very great flints, at length wee came to a place perfectly like an oven curiously clayed round, and in the middest of it a very fayre Urne full of bones very firme and the Urne not rotten, and black ashes a great quantity under the Urne, which is like a butter pott, made of potters earth, but I must not omitt the chiefest thing that at the first opening this Oven one of my Servants thrust in his hand and pulling it quickly back againe I demanding the reason of him, hee told me it was very hott: I did also putt in my hand and it was warme enough to have baked bread: Severall other persons did the like, who can all testifie the trueth of it, this Urne stood in middle of this Oven which I preserve with the bones, but it is since fallen asunder, and digging farther I found sixteene Urnes more but not in ovens, and in the middle one with Eares to it falling into pieces being all full of sound bones and black ashes. I thinke it would puzzle the Royall Societie to give a reason of the heate of the oven being fifteen hundred yeares old. I forbear your further trouble and rest, Sir,

Your most affectionate kinsman
and humble servant, W. Sydenham.[1]
[M. Dr.]

Sydenham to John Locke[2]
[Probably written in 1674]

Your age, ill habitt of body and approach of winter concurring, it comes to pass that the distemper you complaine of yealds not so soone to remedies as it would do under contrary circumstances. However, you may not in the least doubt but that a steddy persisting in the use of the following directions (grounded not on opinion but uninterrupted experience) will at last effect your desired cure. First, therefore, in order to the diverting and subdueing allso the ichorose matter 'twill

[1] The son of Colonel William Sydenham who inherited Wynford Eagle Manor and eventually lost it in a lottery (see *The Manuscripts of the House of Lords*, n.s., 1702–4, vol. v, pp. 15–16).

[2] P.R.O., 30/24/47/2, ff. 11–12. Printed in J. F. Payne, *op. cit.*, pp. 245–6; H. R. Fox Bourne, *op. cit.*, vol. I, pp. 334–5.

be requisite to take your pills twice a weeke as for example every Thursday and Sunday about 4 o'clock in the morning and your clyster in the intermitting days about six, constantly till you are well. In the next place, foreasmuch as there is wanting in bodyes broken with business and dispirited upon the before mentioned accounts, that stock of naturall heat which should bring the matter quickly to digestion, 'twill be highly necessary that you cherish yourself as much as possibly you can be going to bed very early at night, even at 8 o'clock, which next to keeping bed, that is unpracticable, will contributt more to your reliefe than can be imagined. As to diett, all meals of easy digestion and that nourish well may be allowed, provided they be not salt, sweet or spiced, and also excepting fruits, roots and such like. For wine a totall forbearance thereof if it could possibly be, and in its steede the use of any mild small beere, such as our lesser houses do afford, would as near as I can guess be most expedient, for thereby your body would be kept cool, and consequently all accidents proceeding from hott and sharpe humors grating upon the part kept off. As to injections, in your case these things dissuade the use of them:

First your more than ordinary bothe naturall tenderness and delicacy of sense. Then the blood that twice allready hath bin fetched by this operation, which if we are not positively certaine (as how can we be) that it proceeded not from the hurt of the instrument, will (if often repeated) endanger the excoriating the part and making it liable to accidents. Besides they have bin already used (perhaps as often is wont to be don) and this is not a remedy to be long persisted in by the confession of everybody. Sure I am, as I have over and over sayd to you and you know it to be true by my written observations which you have long since seen, that I never use any, where I am concerned alone, there being noe danger nor less certainty of cure in the omitting; and in relation to this business I have now asked myselfe the question what I would doe and have resolved that I would lett them alone.

This is all that I have to offer to you and I have thought of it, and all circumstances relating to your case, with the same intention of mind as if my life and my son's were concern'd therin.

T.S.

Notwithstanding that by this way the cure is certainly to be effected yet nevertheless I observe that in ancient bodyes, especially in the declining part of the year, some little kind of gleeting or moisture (but voide of all malignity) will now and then appear by reason of the weaknesse of the part and will scarce totally vanish till the returne of the warme spring.

Sydenham to John Locke[1]

Sir, I am glad to heare that you are advanced so farr on your way homewards that we may hope to see you here shortly: but I stand amazed at your taking bloud, and as much at the purging you have allready used, and that which you further intend after your ague, which latter would here infallibly returne it upon you, or bring on worse mischiefe. I conceave (and I would myselfe take the same course) it is your best course to doe nothing at all. But in point of diett twill be convenient that you drinke somwhat more liberally wine then before and ride as much as possibly you can. The symptoms you complayne of you ought not to be concerned att, for they are noe other then what are usuall after agues, and ended if you shall so mind them as to obviatt each particulare one you will create to your selfe great danger, they all depending upon one cause, viz., the weakeness of your bloud by the ague, which I am sure nothing will reduce but time and exercise, and even a clyster of milke and sugar will make worse. If you would but ride on horsebacke from Paris to Calis and from Dover to London, upon that and drawing in this aer your symptoms will vanishe.

Since your going hence I have had multiplied experiences of riding long and persisting journies in England, which hath cured more inveteratt distempers than ever yours was, I mean of the longues. I have bin and am still very ill of the gout, pissing of bloud etc., more then a quarter of an year; and having so many distempers broaken in upon very impayred and ill body I am in dispaire of being ever well agayne, and yet I am well content as if I were to live and be well. My service to Dr. Bloamer and his Lady. [I] am most heartily, Your humble servant and very affectionat friend, Tho: Sydenham. [Janu]ery 4° 1677.

Sydenham to Dr. John Mapletoft[2]

Dear Dr., At your [e]arnest request I have thought on the case of the Lady,[3] the fomes[4] of whose distemper I doe not judge to be any ulcer or any venenatt quality else upon the gumm (where it may be supposed some laceration of a nerve was made by that operation) but to be a hystericall quality in the bloud discharging its selfe entirely upon that place and side, where occasion was given by the drawing of the tooth, together with the payne of the operation and the apprehension thereof;

[1] B.L., MS. Locke, c. 19, f. 163. The letter is addressed: "A Madame Madame Blomer chez son excellence l'Embassadeur d'Angleterre a l'Hostel de Turenne a Paris pour fenir a Mr. Locke a Paris." On the back Locke wrote: "4 Jan 77 The time and place".

[2] B.L., MS. Locke, c. 19, f. 164, 1 December, 1677. For forwarding to Locke in Paris.

[3] The Countess of Northumberland, whom Locke treated for trigeminal neuralgia.

[4] A porous substance, absorbent of contagious matter.

for all the ear is to be contracted, after the manner of a clavus[1] in the head, or that other distemper like it, of a violent and exquisitt paine about the temporall[ ][2] which is wont to come and goe, and may, as a clavus, be covered with a shilling.

As to what is to be done, I conceave that bleeding and purging are immediately contraindicated in that they encrease the tumult in the [ ] both are absoluttly necessary in respect of [ ] begining the quieting and settling those vapors [ ] otherwise very often will not admitt thereof, as I know by certaine experience, but after such evacuation easy quietness will doe it. Wherefore were she one of those poor people whom my lott engages me to attend (for I cure not the rich till my being in the grave makes me an Authority) I would take the following course. I would take 8 ounces of bloud from the arme of the affected side. The next morning would give the following pills. Rx. mass. pil. coch. ma: 1 scruple; mercurii dulcis gr. xv; resiad Zalapii gr. iv, balsami Peru. gutt. iii, ms. f. pil. nō. iv. Cap. sume mane:[3] not stirring out of her bedd that day. That night quiett not with Laud. liq. but with Mathewes Pills, they being much better in that they cause a mador the next morning, and so a profitable discharge. The same I would give every night for 3 weekes. The dose is from 14 to 18 graines and are as saff as butter. I would keepe her to milke and water, watergruell, roasted apples and such like fleshless diett for 8 to 10 dayes, to destroy the ferment the sooner. Take heed of irritating the gumm, but rather in extremity of paine lett her hold a pledgett imbued with some dropps of laudanum liq. keeping it between her teeth halfe an houre and then taking in another till her payne cease, which will not be long. If she hath bin allready sufficiently purged, to bleed only may be sufficient and then to come to quieting. When she is out of the fitt lett her guard agaynst the impulse of the disease upon her jawes, by dabbing them with ragg wett with Planten water wherein hath bin dropped spiritt of vitrioll to make itt a little sharp, which by its astrictoriness will defend the part from the deflux better then any thing else; but this must not be don till she hath bin a petty while well of her fitts. This is my opinion, of which make what use you please. I am affectionattly, Yo'r humble servant, Tho: Sydenham. Pell-mell. Dec. 1° 1677.

[The letter ends with this footnote in Dr. Mapletoft's handwriting:]

I thought it best to mention these our Friend's directions for reasons you may know; yet I beleiv'd you would not be displeased to have his opinion too in a case of this difficulty and concernment, which

[1] Painful tumour or excrescence.

[2] Page torn in MS. One word missing shown in square brackets.

[3] Rx. 1 scruple of pilulae cochiae majores, 15 grains of sweet mercury, 4 grains of resiad Jalap, 3 drops of balsam of Peru. Mix. Make 4 pills. Take in the morning.

you may make use of as you find cause. I have sent by Mr. Hill 1 oz. of Mathew's Pill which I have superscribed Philon, Angl. 1 oz. and directed to you. If you think the name will prejudice the advice you may take it upon yourselfe. He advises also a Galbanum plaster to the navell. [On the back Mapletoft has written: "For yourselfe. Lege solus."]

Sydenham to John Locke[1]

Dear Dr., Understanding how much Tabor, now knighted here, hath bin admired for his skill in curing agues, I thought fitt to lett you know a way, if you have not allready observed it in my book, page 99: Tis thus, The fitt being for example on Sonday, lett that fitt pass (it being dangerous to checke the aguish matter that is now ready to be discharged by a paroxisme) and give 2 drams [part cut out][2] Monday morning, 2 drams Monday night, 2 tuesday morning, 2 tuesday night, and you shall be certeyn twill miss comming Wensday. Or thus: Take [cut out] 1 oz. syr ros. sicc., 2 ozs. aut q.s. Take it 4 times as before in the intermitting dayes, drinking a draught of wine after it. If it be a double quarten run over the bastard fitt and give notwithstanding. As in a quarten so in a tertian begin at morning or at night, as soon as the fitt is over (and be sure the next fitt will not come). If a child, then boyle 3 drams [part cut out] in a pint of clarett and give 2 or 3 spoonfuls every third hower. Now to prevent a relaps, be sure to give it agayne ether within 8 or 9 dayes, or if you will, the day after the missing of the first fitt, as thursday morning, thursday night, friday morning, friday night.

Thus you shall be sure to cure, for I never affirmed anything to you which failed. Sic vos non vobis. I never gott 10£ by it, he hath gott 5000. He was an Apothecary in Cambridge wher my booke and practices never much obteyned. Thanke you for my Patient Mr. Robinson.[3] I am most cordially and sincerely your true friend, and affect. servant, Tho. Sydenham. Pall Mall. Aug. 3d. 1678.

If the ague be a new one twill be fitt to purge before you give the powder or stay till it has worn it selfe a little, but if an old one begin presently. I am I thank God perfectly well of my pissing blood, gout etc., and understand my trade somewhat better then when I saw you last, but am yet but a Dunse.

[1] B.L., MS. Locke, c. 19, f. 166, 3 August, 1678.
[2] Locke cut out approximately two words, probably "cortex Peruv".
[3] During his travels in France Locke treated John Robinson (1650–1723) for dysentery. On the latter's return to England Locke advised him to see Sydenham. After a distinguished diplomatic career, Robinson became Bishop of Bristol and London.

Sydenham to John Locke[1]

Sir,

That the exhibiting the cortex hath not met with the same success as here I ascribe to the vomiting the patient; any evacuation whatsoever rendring the medicine ineffectuall. I would advise that you give him a dram thereof, finely powdered and made up with syrup of oranges into a bole every eighthe hour untill he hath taken an ounce drincking a draught of any wine that best likes him after it; and that he be allowed to eat and drinck what best pleases his appetite, excepting onely fruit and all cold liquors. But when he shall have mist two or three fitts and hath strength I wish he were in London under my eye for a few days, provided it consist not with your occasions to be with him, in regard that somewhat is to be don that is a litle nice in order to the preventing accidents that usually follow these things. This is all that I can say upon this subject. Be pleased to present my humble service to Dr. Jacob[2] of whome I have received so good a character of his integrity that I should be verry glad if you could settle an acquaintance between us. I am Sir, Your most affectionate and humble servant, Thos: Sydenham. Pallmall, Aug. 30 [16]79.

Sydenham to John Locke[3]

Dear Sir, Had you observed the counsell which I gave you your patient had by this time been free from the symptoms of dejection of appetite, weakness etc. which you mention. Nor can there be a more expeditious way thought upon to procure his health and your dismission than the giving the C.[4] as I prescribed; and it must still be done for if he have his fitts with what else can you put them away? If he have not them, how else can you prevent their returne, which will certainly happen without the repeating of this medicine every week for two or three weeks longer—he having been reduced to so great a weakness of blood? You must not scruple the allowing him any sort of meat or drinck whatsoever that he desires and his owne pallate will be the best judge what is fit for him; but above all be sure not to use any evacuations of any kinde, and the longer he shall be bound the better it will be for him. This is all I could offer if he were my owne son; but why are you so unkinde to me as that knowing the great obligations I

[1] B.L., MS. Locke, c. 19, f. 167. This letter was sent to Locke whilst he was treating Caleb Banks, his former pupil, during his travels in France.

[2] William Jacob (1623–92), graduated M.D. in 1660 from Christ Church, Oxford.

[3] B.L., MS. Locke, c. 19, f. 168. Addressed: "For my Hon^{y} Freind Dr. Lock, At Mr. Jacob's, an Apothecary in Canterbury."

[4] Cortex Peruvianus (quinine).

have to you to invite me by a promise of making some acknowledgment to give my opinion in this matter? You may command me in everything that you please and shall be obeyed without spoiling that freindship which ceases to be when it ceases to be gratuitous. I am Entirely, Yours, T.S. Pallmall, Sept. 6 1679.

Report to the Earl of Arlington of Physicians Attending his son Lord Ossory[1]

1680 July 28

Since our last my lord's fever hath increased much, with great signs of malignity particularly a great fainting fit, and an eruption of spots all over his body. He hath been delirious these three days, and his water like small beer, and hitherto he hath had no sweats neither could they conveniently be forced by reason of the great burning heat of his head, which hath accompanied his fever.[2] This afternoon his delirium hath somewhat abated, and his pulse keeps up tolerably well, which gives us some hopes. We have treated him with remedies suitable to his condition and shall continue our care and diligence as becomes those who are sensible of the great quality and worth of his person.
[Signed] Tho. Witherley, W. Needham, Th. Sydenham, Ferd. Mendas, Richd. Lower.

Sydenham to Dr. Gould[3]

Sir

I conceive that the salivation though raized by Mercury in your variolous patient doeth noe more contraindicate the giving of Paregoricks than if the same had come on of its own accord in a Confluent Pox and therefor it will be convenient for you to give him every night such a quieting medicine as this. Rx. Aq. Cerasor. nigror, oz. ii., Laudani liq. gut xiiii, Syr. de Mecon. oz. 1½. But if it shall happen that the Mercury shall at any time exert its operation by stooles you may repeat it oftner as there shall be occasion, after the same manner as it might be done in the first days of Mercurial Unctions, where when a Diarrhoea comes on there is noe course soe proper to turn the operation of the Mercury upward & to cause a laudable salivation, as the giving of Laudanum till the Looseness is stopt.

[1] *Calendar of Manuscripts of the Marquess of Ormonde, K.P.*, Historical Manuscripts Commission (1908), n.s., vol. v, pp. 354–5.

[2] The patient died two days after this report was sent to his father. He was probably suffering from typhoid fever.

[3] B.M., Add. MS. 4376, f. 75. Addressed to "Dr. Gould, Fellow of Wadham College, in Oxford". (It is endorsed in a different hand: "December 10 87 letter from Dr. Sydenham about the smallpox under a flux for Venereal Pox".) Printed by John Brown in *Horae Subsecivae*, 1st series (1882), pp. 93–4.

As to what you are pleased to mention concerning the success which youre selfe & others have had in the trying of my Processes, I can only say this, that as I have bin very carefull to write nothing but what was the product of faithfull observation soe when the scandall of my person shall be layd aside and I in my grave it will appear that I neither suffered my selfe to be deceived by indulging to idle speculations nor have deceived others by obtruding any thing upon them but down-right matter of fact. Be pleased to doe me the favour to give my most humble service to Mr. Vice-Chancellor Your Warden whose Father Bp. of Bristoll[1] was my intimate friend and Countryman and I my selfe was once a Fellow-Commoner of your house but how long since I should be glad to know from you as I remember it was in the year that Oxford was surrendered though I had bin of Magdalen Hall some time before.

I am very truely, Sir, Your most humble servant,

Tho. Sydenham.

Pell Mell
Dec. 10: 87.

Sydenham to Major William Hale[2]

Sir,

Though I am perfectly satisfied that your case is only that which in men we call Hypochondriacall, in women Hystericall proceeding from an Ataxy of Shatterednesse of the Animall Spirits & accordingly that a course of steele was a very proper means for you to have bin put under, yet in regard that it have missed of that success which with great reason might have bin expected, I thinke it will be to noe purpose to turn that stone any longer at least after you have taken out the Pills you have allready by you. But 'twill be more adviseable for you for two or three weekes totally to obstain from medicines of all kinds for these two reasons. First for that you have eyther from Dr. Eeles or my selfe charged your body allready with many medecines soe that a little rest from them may be very convenient for you. And then, for that I have often observed that Medicines have not had their due effect whilst they have bin takeing but upon discontinuance the benefit which they have done hath bin manifest. But in case upon tryall for some little time you shall find your symptoms still pressing I doe earnestly entreat you that you will use a remedy which I know you have a prejudice against and

[1] Gilbert Ironside the Elder, Rector of Winterbourne Abbas, near Wynford Eagle, and afterwards Bishop of Bristol.

[2] B.M., Add. MS. 33573, f. 158. Addressed "For the Honoured Major Hale at Kings Walden. Leave this at ye Post house in Hitcham in Hartfordshire". Printed in J. F. Payne, *op. cit.*, pp. 179–81; and by J. D. Comrie, in Thomas Sydenham, *Selected Works* (1922), Plate IV, p. 130 and in Appendix.

which if you had not however you may think not at all indicated in your case and that is the Peruvian Bark. I doe truely affirm to you that as it is as wholesom and innocent as the bread that you dayly eat soe I have seen it succeed in such cases as yours where neither Antiscorbuticks or Steel have effected any thing. If you shall think fit to use this remedy be pleased to give me notice thereof and I shall give order to Mr. Malthus[1] to furnish you with that which I can depend upon & shall like wise insteruct you how to use it. Be pleased to present my most humble service to your Lady, and for your selfe I could heartyly wish instead of a merry Christmas that you might have a smart fit of the Gout which would quickly dissipate your other fears and those symptoms which if I mistake not doe naturally desire a discharge upon the Articles & therefore amongst all tamperings that you may be put upon at any time I doe advise you to beware of bleeding or Purging as diverting this bitter but most effectuall remedy, viz the Gout. I am Sr

Your most humble servant,
Tho. Sydenham.

Pell Mell
December the 17th: 87.

Thomas Sydenham to Anonymous Patient[2]

Sir,

I should be verry glad if it might be that your childs fitt in regard of its tenderness of age would go away of its owne accord, to which purpose were it my owne I thinck I should put the cure upon giving it now and then a large spoonfull of sack, viz. morning, five a clock in the afternoon and at night, but in case upon tryall the fitts shall grow still worse so as to endanger her (for the avoiding of which pray let her not be confined to her bed or chamber) then I desire you to use the barke after this manner. Rx. corticis Peruv: subtiliss: pulv: 2 [drachms] syr: de ros. sicc. q. s. f. elect. in xii partes aeq: dividend: cap^{t}. unam tertiâ vel quartâ quâque horâ solutam in cochl: i. Julap seq: superbib. ejusdem cochl. ii. Rx. Aq: cerasor: nigr: vi. [oz.] cinnamon fort: vi. [drachms] syrup. caryoph: vi. [drachms].[3] You know that the first

[1] Daniel Malthus, Sydenham's apothecary who kept the "Pestle and Mortar" in Pall Mall. He was an ancestor of the Rev. T. Malthus, the political economist.

[2] MS. of Royal College of Physicians. A photographic facsimile of this letter is reproduced in B. Ward Richardson, *Disciples of Aesculapius* (1900), vol. II, p. 671 and transcribed by J. D. Comrie, *op. cit.*, p. 48.

[3] Rx. 2 drachms of finely powdered Peruvian Bark and sufficient syrup of dried roses. Make an electuary. Divide equally into 12 parts. Take one every third or fourth hour dissolved in 1 spoonful of the following Juleb, washing it down with 2 spoonfuls of the same. Rx. 6 ozs. of black cherry water, 6 drachms of strong cinnamon, 6 drachms of syrup of cloves.

dose is to be taken just at the going off of the fitt. This with my humble service to yr Lady is all at present from

Sr yr humble & obliged Servt,
THO. SYDENHAM.

[Marginal note: "Be pleased to give order that she may not be obliged to any dyet, but let her eat and drinck whatever is gratefull to her as at other times."]

Dr. Thomas Molyneux to Locke[1]

Dublin, Aug. 27, 1692.

Sir,

I'm very sensible of your great Civility, in remembering me upon so short an Acquaintance as I had with you in Holland so long time since; and I assure you, without any Compliment, I reckon it amongst the most fortunate Accidents of my Life my so luckily falling into your Conversation, which was so candid, diverting and instructive, that I still reap the Benefit and Satisfaction of it. Some Years after I left you in Holland, upon my Return for *England*, I contracted no small Intimacy with *Dr. Sydenham*, on the Account of having been known to you his much esteemed Friend; and I found him so accurate an Observer of Diseases, so thoroughly skill'd in all useful Knowledge of his Profession, and withal so communicative, that his Acquaintance was a very great Advantage to me: And all this I chiefly owe to you, Sir, besides the Information of many useful Truths, and a great deal of very pleasing Entertainment I have met with, in the Perusal of your lately publish'd Writings: So that on many Accounts I must needs say there are very few Men in the World, to whom I can with the like Sincerity profess my self to be, as I am

Dear Sir
Your most real Friend, and
very humble and obliged Servant,
Tho. Molyneux.

Locke to Dr. Thomas Molyneux[2]

Oates, Nov. 1, 1692.

Sir,

The Indisposition of my Health, which drove me out of London, and keeps me still in the Country, must be an Excuse for my so long Silence. The very great Civility you express to me in your Letter,

[1] *Familiar Letters between Mr. John Locke and Several of his Friends* (4th ed., 1742), p. 218.
[2] *Ibid.*, pp. 219–20.

makes me hope your Pardon for the Slowness of my Answer, whereby I hope you will not measure the Esteem and Respect I have for you. That your own distinguishing Merit, amongst the rest of my Country-men I met with at Leyden, has so settled in me, that before the Occasion your Brother's Favour lately gave me to inquire after you, I often remember'd you; and 'twas not without Regret I consider'd you at a Distance, that allow'd me not the Hopes of renewing and improving my Acquaintance with you. There being nothing of Value so much as ingenious, knowing Men, think it not strange that I laid hold on the first Opportunity, to bring my self again into your Thoughts. You must take it as an Exercise of your Goodness, drawn on you by your own Merit: For whatever Satisfaction I gain to my self in having recover'd you again, I can propose no Advantage to you, in the Offer of a very useless and infirm Acquaintance, who can only boast that he very much esteems you.

That which I always thought of Dr. Sydenham living, I find the World allows him now he is dead, and that he deserved all that you say of him. I hope the Age has many who will follow his Example, and by the way of accurate practical Observation, as he has so happily begun, enlarge the History of Diseases, and improve the Art of Physick; and not, by speculative Hypotheses, fill the World with useless, though pleasing Visions. Something of this kind permit me to promise my self one Day from your judicious Pen. I know nothing that has so great an Encouragement from the Good of Mankind as this. . . .

J. Locke.

Dr. Thomas Molyneux to Locke[1]

Dublin, Dec. 20, 1692.

Sir,

I'm much concerned to hear you have your Health no better; and, on this Occasion, cannot but deplore the great Loss the intellectual World, in all Ages, has suffer'd by the strongest and soundest Minds possessing the most infirm and sickly Bodies. Certainly there must be some very powerful Cause for this in Nature, or else we could not have so many Instances, where the Knife cuts the Sheath, as the *French* materially express it: And if so, this must be reckon'd among the many other inseparable Miseries that attend human Affairs.

I could wish the Physicians Art were so powerful and perfect, as in some measure to prevent so great an Evil; but we find where once Nature, or the *Œconomia Animalis* of the body is so depraved as not

[1] *Familiar Letters between Mr. John Locke and Several of his Friends* (4th ed., 1742) pp. 220–2.

to co-operate with Medicine, all Remedies, and the Courses of them, prove wholly ineffectual, or to very little Purpose. But still the more imperfect Physick is, so much the more is owing to those who the least improve so difficult a Province, which certainly has been considerably advanced by some late *English* Authors. And that puts me in mind to desire of your Thoughts, or what other learned Physicians you converse with say, concerning Dr. *Morton*, and his late *Exercitations on Fevers*. As for his *General Theory* of them, I esteem it, as all others of this kind, a sort of mere waking Dream, that Men are strangely apt to fall into, when they think long of a Subject, beginning quite at the wrong End; for by framing such Conceits in their Fancies, they vainly think to give their Understandings Light, whilst the Things themselves are still, or perhaps ever must remain, in Darkness.

In his first Exercitation that treats of *Agues*, I don't find he has said any thing very material, or worth Notice, that the World did not sufficiently know before; unless it were some Histories of the irregular Shapes and Symptoms this Distemper appears under, which I thinke may be very instructive to the Physician, and of great Ease and Advantage to the Sick.

But his practical Remarks in his second Exercitation about *continuing* and *remitting* Fevers, if they be judiciously founded upon many and steady Observations, so that they may safely pass into a Rule, must certainly be of great Moment in directing the Management and Cure of Fevers. I confess my Experience in this Distemper, as yet, falls something too short for to determine positively whether all his Observations be real and well grounded; but, as far as I can judge at present, several of them do hold good.

I remember to have heard Dr. *Morton* was once a *Presbyterian* Preacher: And though he were, this does not make him a Jot the less capable in above twenty Years Practice to have carefully observed the Accidents that naturally occur in the Progress of a Disease; and if he be but a true and judicious Register, 'tis all I desire from him.

You see I have taken great Freedom in giving a Character according to my Apprehension of this Author, but 'tis only to encourage you to use the same Liberty; for if at your Leisure you would let me know your own Thoughts, or what other candid Men say concerning him, and his Methods of Cure, or any other useful Tract that comes abroad, you will extremely oblige,

Sir
Your very obedient
humble servant,
T. Molyneux.

Locke to Dr. Thomas Molyneux[1]

Oates, Jan. 20 1692/3.

Sir,

. . . The Doctor, concerning whom you enquire of me, had, I remember, when I liv'd in Town, and convers'd among the Physicians there, a good Reputation amongst those of his own Faculty. I can say nothing of his late Book of *Fevers*, having not read it my self, nor heard it spoke of by others: But I perfectly agree with you concerning general Theories, that they are for the most part but a sort of waking Dreams, with which, when Men have warm'd their own Heads, they pass into unquestionable Truths, and then the ignorant World must be set right by them: Though this be, as you rightly observe, beginning at the wrong End, when Men lay the Foundation in their own Fancies, and then endeavour to suit the Phoenomena of Diseases, and the Cure of them, to those Fancies. I wonder, that after the Pattern Dr. *Sydenham* has set them of a better Way, Men should return again to that Romance Way of Physick. But I see it is easier and more natural for Men to build Castles in the Air of their own, than to survey well those that are to be found standing. Nicely to observe the History of Diseases, in all their Changes and Circumstances, is a Work of Time, Accurateness, Attention and Judgment; and wherein if Men, through Prepossession or Oscitancy, mistake, they may be convinced of their Error by unerring Nature and Matter of Fact, which leaves less room for the Subtlety and Dispute of Words, which serves very much instead of Knowledge in the learned World, where methinks Wit and Invention has much the Preference to Truth. Upon such Grounds as are the establish'd History of Diseases, *Hypotheses* might with less Danger be erected, which I think are so far useful, as they serve as an Art of Memory to direct the Physician in particular Cases, but not to be rely'd on as Foundations of Reasonings, or Verities to be contended for; they being, I think I may say all of them, Suppositions taken up *gratis*, and will so remain, till we can discover how the natural Functions of the Body are performed, and by what Attraction of the Humours or Defects in the Parts they are hinder'd or disorder'd. To which purpose I fear the *Galenists* four Humours, or the Chymists *Sal*, *Sulphur*, and *Mercury*, or the late prevailing Invention of *Acid* and *Alcali*, or whatever hereafter shall be substituted to these with new Applause, will upon Examination be found to be but so many learned empty Sounds, with no precise, determinate Signification. What we know of the works of Nature, especially in the Constitution of Health, and

[1] *Familiar Letters between Mr. John Locke and Several of his Friends* (4th ed., 1742), pp. 223–4.

the Operations of our own Bodies, is only by the sensible Effects, but not by any Certainty we can have of the Tools she uses, or the Ways she works by. So that there is nothing left for a Physician to do, but to observe well, and so by Analogy argue the like Cases, and thence make to himself Rules of Practice: And he that is this way most sagacious, will, I imagine, make the best Physician, though he should entertain distinct Hypotheses concerning distinct Species of Diseases, subservient to this End, that were inconsistent one with another, they being made use of in these several Sorts of Diseases, but as distinct Arts of Memory in those Cases. And I the rather say this, that they might be rely'd on only as artificial Helps to a Physician, and not as Philosophical Truths to a Naturalist. But, Sir, I run too far, and must beg your Pardon for talking so freely on a Subject you understand so much better than I do. I hoped the Way of treating Diseases, which with so much Approbation Dr. *Sydenham* had introduced into the World, would have beaten the other out, and turned Men from Visions and Wrangling to Observation, and endeavouring after settled Practices in more Diseases, such as I think he has given us in some. If my Zeal for saving Mens Lives, and preserving their Health (which is infinitely to be preferr'd to any Speculations ever so fine in Physick) has carried me too far, you will excuse it in one who wishes well to the Practice of Physick, though he meddles not with it. I wish you and your Brother, and all yours, a very happy New Year, and am

Sir,

your most humble and faithful servant

John Locke.

Index

Index